Doctors'

Legacy

A SELECTION OF PHYSICIANS' LETTERS

1721-1954

Edited by LAURENCE FARMER, M.D.

FOREWORD BY LEONA BAUMGARTNER, M.D., PH.D.

H|B

HARPER & BROTHERS   PUBLISHERS   NEW YORK

Library of Congress catalog card number: 54-12176

CONTENTS

FOREWORD

A patient is always interested in his doctor's personal opinions, but seldom does he have a chance to learn about them. Seldom, too, do doctors record them. For these reasons and because of the range of personalities and periods covered, the present collection of personal letters of physicians is a unique literary contribution. Here doctors express frankly their ideas on death, cancer, psychiatry, women in medicine, socialized medicine, quackery, religion and many other subjects.

The time covered runs from 1721 to 1954. Some of the best-known physicians in the history of medicine are represented as well as a number who are less well known. The introductory material of each letter puts it into its historical setting and adds enormously to the reader's pleasure.

The collection will interest the professional man and the layman, the historian and the sociologist, the biographer and the common reader—all who would like to learn something of the personalities and attitudes of men whose human and social insight has developed through the practice of the medical profession.

LEONA BAUMGARTNER, M.D., Ph.D.
Commissioner of Health, New York City

ACKNOWLEDGMENTS

The letters reproduced in this book have been selected from various sources and many have been made available to me through the courtesy of private individuals, publishing firms, publications and libraries to all of whom I extend my sincere thanks. In particular I am indebted to:

George Allen & Unwin, Ltd., London, for material from Greville Macdonald's *Reminiscences of a Specialist*;

Dr. J. C. Bacala, for his unpublished letter;

J.-B. Baillière et Fils, for the selection from Léon Délhoume's *Jean Cruveilhier*, and Alfred Rouxeau' *Laennec avant 1806*.

Dr. William B. Bean, for making available the letter by Dr. Saul Jarcho;

Basic Books Inc., Publishers, New York, for letters by Sigmund Freud from *The Origins of Psycho-analysis*, edited by Marie Bonaparte, Anna Freud, Ernst Kris. Translation by Eric Mosbacher and James Strachey;

Chatto and Windus, Ltd., London, for selections from *Letters of Anton Tchekhov to his Family and Friends*. Translation by Constance Garnett;

The Clarendon Press, Oxford, for material from Sir Rickman J. Godlee's *Lord Lister*;

Constable & Co., Ltd., London, for the selection from *Life and Letters of Joseph Black* by Sir William Ramsay;

Duke University Press, Durham, N.C., for material from *Letters of Richard D. Arnold*, edited by Richard H. Shryock;

Dr. Leslie A. Falk for his letter to *The Journal of the American Medical Association*;

Dr. John F. Fulton for the letters by Arnold C. Klebs and for a letter from his biography of Harvey Cushing;

John Grieve, F.R.C.S., for the permission to use his letter to *The Lancet*;

The Journal of the American Medical Association, Chicago, for the letters by Doctors Leslie A. Falk and Frederic S. Sharpless;

Hahnsche Buchhandlung, Hannover, for selections from *Briefe von Theodor Billroth*;

Dr. Robert B. Hoenig for his unpublished letter to his parents;

Houghton Mifflin Co., Boston, for letters from *Life and Correspondence of Henry Ingersoll Bowditch* by Vincent Y. Bowditch, and from James Jackson Putnam's *Memoir of Dr. James Jackson*;

Jackson–Son & Co. (Booksellers), Ltd., Glasgow, as successors to James MacLehose & Sons for a selection from the *Life of Sir William Tennant Gairdner* by G. A. Gibson;

Dr. Saul Jarcho for his unpublished letter to Dr. William B. Bean;

Dr. Robert E. Kaufman for unpublished letter to his son;

The Lancet, London, for material from its correspondence columns (letters by John Grieve, Alex E. Roche, W. G. Burnie, Edgar Trevithick and two unidentified physicians);

Lea & Febiger, Publishers, Philadelphia, for the selection from C.-E. A. Winslow's *Life of Hermann M. Biggs*;

Library Co. of Philadelphia for the letters by Benjamin Rush to William Claypoole and James Rush, the originals of which are in its possession;

Library of the New York Academy of Medicine for the letters by Carl Beck, William Hunter, Sir Henry Thompson, the originals of which are in its possession, and for the copies of the letters by Hendrick van Beuren, Oliver Wendell Holmes and David Hosack;

Dr. David R. Lyman for his letter to Dr. Charles J. Hatfield;

Lord Patrick D. Moynihan and Mrs. Elsie Bateman for the letters from Donald Bateman's *Berkeley Moynihan, Surgeon*;

Dr. Charles F. Mullett for the material from his *Letters of George Cheyne to Samuel Richardson* (1733-1743);

The New England Journal of Medicine, Boston, for the letters from its pages by Drs. J. Jerrold Applegarth and Lowis W. Palfrey;

The New York Historical Society for the selections from the *Cadwallader Colden Papers* in *Collections of the New York Historical Society*;

Dr. Alton Ochsner for his unpublished letter;

G. P. Putnam's Sons, New York, for the material from *Life and Letters of Mary Putnam Jacobi* by Ruth Putnam, copyright 1925;

Alex E. Roche, F.R.C.S., for the permission to use his letter to *The Lancet*;

Mr. Edwin A. Salmon for the letters from *Thomas W. Salmon, Psychiatrist* by Earl D. Bond;

The Society of Medical History of Chicago for the letter by William Matthews from its *Bulletin*;

The Spectator, London, for the letter by Sir William Osler;

Charles C. Thomas, Publisher, Springfield, Illinois, for the selection from John F. Fulton's *Harvey Cushing*.

To the members of the Library Staff of the New York Academy of medicine whose untiring and continued co-operation has been invaluable I express my special thanks and appreciation.

L. F.

Doctors' Legacy

INTRODUCTION

Much has been written and said, by nonmedical people, about physicians and the practice of medicine. Some of it is laudatory, much very critical. Neither the praise nor the criticism has full validity since both are usually tinged by personal bias and often based on emotional reactions. It is not difficult to imagine what kind of experiences caused Voltaire or Bernard Shaw to make their scathing remarks about medical men, nor to visualize the kind of physicians Robert Louis Stevenson must have encountered when he wrote his glowing eulogy of them.

Physicians themselves have also had much to say about their vocation and their colleagues. They are not necessarily more objective in their judgments but at least they have a better insight into the subject matter under discussion.

In the following letters physicians have written about many of their problems. They have written about the practice of their profession, about their patients, about themselves. They have discussed their ethics and their religious beliefs, their hopes and their disappointments, their aspirations and their disillusionments. In some of the letters the men who made medical history have told of their discoveries, in others physicians have described the impact of these discoveries upon themselves. Some of the letter writers were the most famous physicians of their day, others we would no longer know were it not for their letters.

The period covered by this selection starts with the eighteenth century—when medicine as we know it today began to evolve—and it reaches up to the present time. During these centuries the letter writers were faced by greatly differing conditions. Their comments furnish a picture of the changing medical scene.

Through the ages man's attempts at combating disease reflect the prevailing intellectual climate. At the dawn of our racial history when spirits and demons were held responsible for man's fate, incantations, exhortations and prayers were the appropriate means of treatment. The judicious use of other measures, with more tangible effects, a splint applied to a fractured leg, concoctions from berries or leaves, would be, on occasion, helpful adjuncts to the psychosomatic practices of the tribal medicine man.

From the realm of magic the art of healing moved into the sphere of religion and thence into that of philosophical speculation. Medical practice remained a strange mixture of mysticism and superstition tempered by small doses of rationalism and empiricism. Gradually there accumulated, over the millennia, a body of knowledge based on the observation of healthy and sick persons which provided the Egyptian, Greek and Roman physicians of Antiquity with methods of treatment differing greatly from those of the medicine man. But, still, medicine was very imperfect since it had no clear insight into the functioning of the body. Whatever degree of refinement the art of healing attained at this period was destroyed when, in the wake of the invasions of the Germanic barbarians, darkness descended on the Western World. Ignorance, superstition and mysticism again dominated the practice of medicine.

With the revival of learning in Europe during the Renaissance a more rational approach again came to the fore. But the art of healing long remained very primitive. For diagnosis physicians relied largely on gazing at the urine, for therapy on bleeding, purging and sweating and the use of medicinal agents which ran the gamut from herbs and other plants through cockroaches and worms to all kinds of animal excrements. A fifteenth-century prescription recommended a potion of goat droppings in red wine for the treatment of bloody urine, and another earthworms with yellow knots, ground with saffron, for jaundice. When Lorenzo the Magnificent lay on his deathbed at Florence, in 1492, a famous physician was called in on consultation who prescribed an elixir of ground pearls. Naturally the patient was one of the wealthiest men of his day. Less affluent people had to be satisfied with more modest medicines. And many a man still subscribed to Roger Bacon's view that ". . . a physician who knows not to take into account the positions and aspects of the planets can effect nothing in the healing arts except by chance and good fortune." Little wonder that the great satirist Rabelais, himself a physician, should have spoken of the practice of medicine as "but a farce played by three actors: the physician, the patient and the disease."

Not that progress was not being made. The anatomical studies of Andreas Vesalius in the sixteenth century, the discovery of the circulation of the blood by William Harvey in the seventeenth, the invention of the microscope and its application to medical studies by van Leeuwenhoek and others were great steps forward. By the middle of the eighteenth century astrology and the therapeutic use of cockroaches and the ground bones of hanged criminals had been abandoned, at least by reputable practitioners, but medicine was still crude and ineffectual.

Surgery, restricted mainly to amputations, was a dreadful ordeal which terminated more often in the death of the patient than in his recovery. Childbirth was fraught with the danger of infection and infant mortality was appallingly high. Contagious and infectious diseases still were among the greatest killers of man. Their nature and origin were not understood and there was no treatment for their victims. Some of these diseases, like cholera and typhus fever, were ever-present, especially in prisons and slums; occasionally they would take on epidemic proportions and run a devastating course. The outcome of Napoleon's fateful campaign in 1812 was decided more by the ravages of typhus fever among his troops than by the strategy of the Russians. Others, like plague, appeared suddenly and mysteriously, seemingly from nowhere, decimating whole populations. In Pericles' times this scourge, the "Black Death," decided the fate of Athens; in the Middle Ages it spread like wildfire through all of Europe, striking even the staunchest with terror and despair. It was, truly, the "Wrath of God." Smallpox perennially killed and disfigured high and low by the tens of thousands, tuberculosis was widespread, so was syphilis, and diphtheria took its heavy toll of small children.

Not able to overcome the difficulties arising from the paucity of factual knowledge medical men had long been given to speculation. These speculations had taken on elaborate dimensions. New "schools" and "systems" were being constantly evolved and their adherents engaged in heated and often acrimonious controversies. Animists, vitalists, iatrochemists, homeopaths were all convinced of the infallibility of their special theory and had the greatest contempt for one another and for everyone else. Many physicians and educated laymen were greatly concerned about this state of affairs. Thomas Jefferson, writing to a physician friend about his "scepticism in medicine" commented scathingly that he himself had lived ". . . to see the disciples of Hoffman, Boerhaave, Stahl, Cullen, Brown succeed one another like the shifting figures of a magic lantern, and their fancies, like the dresses of the annual doll-babies from Paris, becoming, from their novelty, the vogue of the day, and yielding to the next novelty their ephemeral favor." And the patient, ". . . treated on the fashionable theory, sometimes gets well in spite of the medicine." As far as the latter was concerned Dr. Oliver Wendell Holmes, an astute physician, once said that he "firmly" believed that if all the medicines then used could be "sunk to the bottom of the sea, it would be all the better for mankind,—and all the worse for the fishes."

Such was the status of medical science and practice when our early letter writers penned their communications almost 250 years ago. How much medicine has since changed will become evident from their subsequent correspondence. Their letters also document how much their aspirations, their ethics, their human reactions and they themselves have remained the same.

WILLIAM DOUGLASS (1691-1752)

On completing his medical studies at Edinburgh and Leyden, outstanding universities of his day, Dr. William Douglass emigrated to the American Colonies. After wandering about for several years, he finally, in 1718, settled in Boston, where he soon had a lucrative practice. But conditions were apparently not very much to his liking and it seems that it would have taken but little to induce him to move on. Early in 1721 we find him writing to a friend in New York, Dr. Cadwallader Colden, a Scottish physician who like himself had come to the New World.

To Cadwallader Colden, M.D.

Boston. February 20, 17$\frac{20}{21}$

. . . You complain of the Practice of Physick being undervalued in your parts and with reason; we are not much better in that respect in this place; we abound with Practi[ti]oners tho no other graduate than my self, we have 14 Apothecary shops in Boston, all our Practi[ti]oners dispense their own medicines, my self excepted being the first who hath lived here by Practice without the advantage of advance on Medicines. . . . I have resolved to fix here and ramble no more. I can live handsomely by the incomes of my Practice, and save some small matter. I reckon this place at present no better than a factory as to my interest, for here we have a great trade and many strangers with

7

whom my business chiefly consists. I have here practice amongst four sorts of People some familys pay me 5£ per annum each for advice sick or well, some few fee me as in Britain, but for the Native New Englanders I am oblidged to keep a day book of my Consultations advice and Visits and bring them in a Bill, others of the poorer Sort I advise and Visit without any expectation of fees. . . .

A few months later, after a respite of nineteen years, the dread smallpox suddenly appeared in Boston. The populace was terror-stricken, the medical profession helpless. At the height of the expanding epidemic, the Reverend Cotton Mather, of dubious witch-hunting fame, began advocating a new method of smallpox prophylaxis. He soon found followers, especially in view of the helplessness of many of the most competent medical practitioners who could give no better advice than to "give no disturbance by medicine" and to "let nature take its course."

The method in question, which consisted of inoculating healthy individuals with pus from the blisters of smallpox sufferers, had recently become known in England through Lady Mary Wortley Montagu, the impetuous wife of the British Ambassador in Constantinople. During her stay in the Near East, where this practice had originated, Lady Montagu had become so enthusiastic about it that she had submitted her children to inoculation and, on her return to England, she had persuaded others to follow her example.

Under prodding from Cotton Mather and other clergymen, Dr. Zabdiel Boylston now started smallpox inoculation in Boston. The majority of the medical profession, under the leadership of William Douglass, vehemently opposed its use, arguing that its efficacy was far from proven and that it was fraught with danger. The public took sides, and soon the small community was shaken to its foundations by a controversy which almost led to bloodshed and brought Mather and Boylston in jeopardy of their lives. Gradually the epidemic subsided and tempers cooled. Writing to Colden, Douglass gives a vivid description of the course of inoculation in healthy individuals and he tells of the reasons for his opposition to this practice.

To Cadwallader Colden, M.D.

Boston, May 1, 1722

. . . After 19 years intermission, we received, via Salt— Tartudas from Barb   the small Pox midle of April 1721, and by Jan. Following it was near over having affected only Boston and two or three adjacent Towns. . . .

. . . Whereof, some have been Inoculated oftener than once before it took effect, with some it never wrought; they all complained much of Head disorders and stupers even those who had but very few & these imperfect Pustules; their incisions grew up in a few days as in common superficial wounds of the skin, but about the 7th or 8 day generally they begin to complain (some few sooner or latter), are feverish, their incisions inflame open and discharge profusely, with a peculiar noxious fetor and continue running some weeks after their small Pox Pimples are dryd up and they abroad about their affairs infect wherever they go (this spreading of Infection and consequently rending it more intense is a great objection against Inoculation practised at random in a place where greatest part of the People are lyable to the distemper). . . . What the consequences may be and if some of them may not be lyable to the small Pox in the natural way, time only can determine. But to speak candidly for the present, it seems to be somewhat more favourable received by Inoculation than received the natural way. I opposed this novel and dubious Practice not being sufficiently oppined of its safety, and consequences, in short I reckond it a sin against society to propagate infection by this means and bring on my neighbour a distemper which might prove fatal which perhaps he might escape (as many have done) in the ordinary way, which he might certainly secure himself against by removal in this Country where it prevails seldom. However many of our Clergy had got into it and they scorn to retract, I had them to oppose which occasioned great heats (you may perhaps admire how they reconcile this with their doctrine of Predestination); the Inclosed Pamphlets which unwillingly I was oblidged to publish, may inform you more at large of the controversy, . . .

GEORGE CHEYNE (1671-1743)

Medicine at the beginning of the eighteenth century had little insight into the functions of the healthy body or the nature of disease, and its methods of diagnosis were extremely limited. Little wonder that the treatment of the sick was generally ineffectual.

Dr. George Cheyne, a well-known Scottish physician of this period, had received a good classical and medical education. He had some extreme views, especially on the role of diet in the treatment of disease, but he may be regarded as a well-informed, although somewhat doctrinaire, physician.

Much sought-after by many important persons, Cheyne was the physician also of Samuel Richardson, the author of *Pamela* and *Clarissa*, whom he treated for what appears to have been high blood pressure, a disease then as yet unrecognized.

To Samuel Richardson

Bath April 20, 1740

... Your present Complaint, as you very accurately describe it, is entirely nervous from Wind in the Primae Viae and Membranes of the Muscles and is of no Manner of dangerous consequence. If it comes to any Height so as to produce Terror or Confusion of inattention to Business your only present Relief is a Tea Spoonful or two of the Tincture of Soot, and Assa Foetida made on Peony Water in a cold Infusion drunk any

Time in a Glass of Peper Mint Water Simple. This will make you break Wind plentifully and so relieve you. I have had that Complaint now and these Twenty Years, and thought and thought the Walls and Floor of the House playing up and down with me, but the solid Cure is a Vomit every now and then; especially when very bad about new Moon, but when tolerable twice a Year, Michaelmas and Lady-day. In short, your total Case is Scurbutico Nervose from a sedentary studious Life.

I wonder you get not the Chamber-horse which is now so universally known and practiced in all the studious Professions in London. It is certainly admirable and has all the good and beneficial Effects of a hard Trotting Horse except the fresh Air. I ride an Hour every Morning and will do more when Weather will not permit me to walk in my Garden or ride in my Coach. (Only remember the Board ought to be as long as the Room will permit 18 or 20 Feet 16 at least, and the Chair you sit on with a Cushion on the Board as a Bottom to it with a two armed Hoop and with a Foot-stool that with a sliding Board may be raised higher or lower.) It may be bought for a Couple of Pounds and is more necessary for Children or aged Persons than a Bed or a Cradle. You may dictate, direct, or read in it and it rides double better than single. I have found great Benefit by it. I desire you'll begin your cold Bath again forthwith; it cleanses as well as contracts. Your Diet is quite right, being that of the temperate healthy which though it may admit of Disorders can produce no first mortal Distemper. I think a Glass, 2 or 3 at most, of good Raisin Wine, especially with Elder Berries the very best of all Cordials. But surely Wine was never designed for common Beverage as now used but as a Medicine or as a bitter Draught for the common Encouragement from Revelation by St. Paul to Timothy plainly implies.

. . . In the Spring you'll grow better and stronger towards Midsummer and till Michaelmas, and then you must careen again;

but good Blood is City Security for long life and Health. I thank you again and again for my valuable Present, and am with Truth and Warmth   Dear Sir

> Your sincere Wellwisher and Thankfull Servant
> Geo. Cheyne

Be sure to take a Scotch or Gum Pill or two once a Week.

To Samuel Richardson

Bath, April 26, 1742

I have yours of to Day and am glad you are no worse. The Spring Season, the Badness of the Blood, the long Easterly Winds, and frosty Mornings will readily account for your late Paroxism. . . . I am only concerned for the Lowness of your Spirits and that you cannot bear Company or Amusement. As to Medicine, in that Case and also to help your Sleep, I never found any Thing effectual but Pills made of true Assa Foetida washed down with Pepper Mint or Rue Water with a few drops of the Tincture of Soot in it. . . .

I have been often under that Terror and Anxiety you mention and always suffered to Extremity if the Chariot was accidentally stopped. Drilling along I found to be the best Day Time Opiate to my Anguish, and I could have wished I could have lived, eat, drunk, and slept in a Vehicle. I wish you could bear the Thumb Vomits in a Morning though it bring up Nothing. It is the best Exercise and an internal Squeezer at that Time. I would fain wish you to get rid of all Doctors, Drugs, and Apothecaries. Chanon is certanly an honest, ingenious, and descreet Person. But a Horse and an Ass (the two best Doctors in Europe as Dr. Garth used to say) you must not think to part with, cost what they will.

. . . your Disorders are vastly like my own, only I began earlier to manage my Diet, but for Vomits I believe I took some Hundreds of them, and never lost my Appetite, Sleep, or Spirits, but I found no Peace or Ease till I had recourse to them . . . all my nervous Patients that have been long and obstinately ill of Scurbutico-Nervous Distempers, have ever told, there was no quick or so [   ] Relief but Vomits of one Kind or another. As to your Diet, be assured the Bread or Seed Meats are the best of any in your present Disorder. If you can get Asses Milk where you are I could wish you to drink half a Pint of it every Morning, . . . It is the best Sweetener, Cooler, and Thinner of bad Blood; a few Drops of Spirit of Hartshorn in it, would improve it; at Dinner Rice Pudding, and at Night Watergruel or Milk Porridge. As to the Quantity no Rule can be ascertained; to be sure the less the better. Never to fill the Stomach nor load the Nerves, a Pound at the Dinner Meal, and half a Pound at the Supper Meal I think a just Mediocrity, with Tea and Toast and Water for Beverage.

I wish you would take some Amusement to pass off this dark dismal Time. If you could, like the Swallows, dose out in forgetfulness or Indolence such a Winter Season with the Swallows and Nightingales; like them you would be alive in the Spring and chant and fly. I had a Friend that advised me to write Books at such a Time, or to read or have read to me innocent, interesting Stories, Novels or Plays. The Thing I like at best was with one or two domestic Friends or Acquaintances of my own Way of Thinking, to play at push Pin, Quadrill, or Picquet, or Tables. Something you ought to contrive to kill Time, for under God you cannot fail to do well in Time, but Nothing but Time, your Diet, and Exercise can do it, could you give your Life for it.

Get rid of Doctors and all the quacking Trade as soon as you can. I find few of them that understands your Case. I have tried all their Medicines in my own Bacon, which is more instructing than any Thing can be known in anothers. As to Fits, Paroxisms, and Plunges, when they happen your Family and Friends will oblige to bear them, but get rid [of them] as soon as you can. . . . I well know, that a new Medicine and a new Doctor is a kind of a Cordial in such Cases. . . .

JOHN MITCHELL (died 1768)

The practice of medicine in Colonial America was arduous. Already difficult under the prevailing primitive conditions, the novelty of many diseases, the extraordinary course of others, and the often adverse effect of the unaccustomed climatic conditions upon the settlers all contributed to make it even more trying. A faint idea of the magnitude of the problems and of their impact upon the pioneer doctor is conveyed by the following letter.

The writer, Dr. John Mitchell, a learned physician and accomplished scientist, had come to America as a young man and had settled in Virginia. His concept of his profession and of his obligations to it and to his patients was extremely high. The strain under which he toiled was too great for him. After twenty years, middle-aged and broken in health, he returned to England.

To Cadwallader Colden, M.D.

Virginia, Urbanna, Sept. 10, 1745

. . . There is another thing which you seem to request of me, concerning the yellow fever; which is, to publish my Account of it. That I cannot by any means do, at least at this time, & am uncertain if ever I shall. But that I may not seem to you to act without reason, I shall give you, who are such a master of Reason, a very good reason for it. You know, that this is but one of many Diseases, that are either peculiar to our Climes, or vary their natures so, as hardly to be known, and to be harder to Cure, by those that are unacquainted with their peculiar Causes, natures &c. among us; or with the nature of the common things, air, water, Situation, &c. in this our new world; or how our Constitutions are affected, & entirely altered by them, at least in these more Southern Latitudes. All these I have had to enquire into, before I thought I could discharge my duty, to those who trusted their Lives to my care. Many other things, as the natures & qualities of Minerals, Vegetables & Animals are necessary to establish our art on a good foundation. In short the whole System of Nature must be fathomed by him, who would qualify himself for the sublime art of healing. But my office & business in the world is to know & understand as much of those things as I can, in order to apply them, & not to teach them; Enough, shall I say, or too much, for any one Man to do! at least I have found it too much for me; when joyned to the fatigues of such a slavish Practice, as you know ours is. . . .

OLIVER GOLDSMITH (1728-1774)

The medical career of the author of *The Vicar of Wakefield* was brief and undistinguished and for the most part obscure.

After his preliminary education, Oliver Goldsmith matriculated in the University of Edinburgh from where he went to the Continent to continue his medical studies. And then the record becomes dim. When and where he graduated is not clear. Two years after leaving Edinburgh we find him back in London practicing in a poor section, obviously unable to make both ends meet. He then applied for the position of hospital mate, but did not qualify. Nothing more was heard of him as a medical man.

A letter written to his uncle, the Reverend Thomas Contarine, makes one regret that he gave up medicine so soon, for he combined a clear understanding of what constitutes a good physician with a feeling for the dignity of his profession.

To the Reverend Thomas Contarine

1753

. . . Since I am upon so pleasing a topic as self applause, give me leave to say that the circle of science which I have run through, before I undertook the study of physic, is not only useful, but absolutely necessary to the making a skilful physician. Such sciences enlarge our understanding, and sharpen our sagacity; and what is a practitioner without both but an empiric, for never yet was a disorder found entirely the same in two patients. A quack, unable to distinguish the particularities in each disease, prescribes at a venture: if he finds such a disorder may be called by the general name of fever for instance, he has a set of remedies which he applies to cure it, nor does he desist till his medicines are run out, or his patient has lost his life. But the skilful physician distinguishes the symptoms, manures the sterility of nature, or prunes her luxuriance; nor does he depend so much on the efficacy of medicines as on their proper application. . . .

. . . I have spent more than a fortnight every second day at the Duke of Hamilton's, but it seems they like me more as a *jester* than as a companion; so I disdained so servile an employment; 'twas unworthy my calling as a physician.

I have nothing new to add from this country; and I beg, dear Sir, you will excuse this letter, so filled with egotism. I wish you may be revenged on me, by sending an answer filled with nothing but an account of yourself.

JOSEPH BLACK (1728-1799)

Practical experience, based on sound theoretical knowledge, is nowhere possibly as essential as in medicine. The young medical man, with the practical mind, who recognized this so early in his career, later became one of the great names in chemistry, a science then in its infancy and from which modern medicine was to profit so greatly.

That Joseph Black, the writer of the following letter, did not have only a practical mind, but also a very methodical one, is amusingly documented by his will. A life-long bachelor, it was found upon his death that he had bequeathed his fortune in ten thousand equal legacies.

To his father

Edinburgh, June 1, 1754

... I am not yet installed into the order of the great wig, but have gone through all the examinations, & nothing is wanting but the ceremony. ...

In my last letter to you I proposed to go immediately to London to spend some time in the Hospitals there. ... I have now studied the Theory of medicine & have likewise been taught every thing upon the Practice which can be learned in a College. I have also seen some real Practice & have even practised a little myself. But all this is not enough. I should be thoroughly acquainted with the real Practice & this is a thing very different from what can be learned in a College; thus for instance we are taught by our Professors that if a sick person breathes with great difficulty, one thing must be done; if his respiration is yet more laborious, another. But How shall we judge of the nice degrees of laborious breathing unless from a dayly & familiar acquaintance with, & study of, the appearances and looks of Patients &c. Most young Physicians neglect this essential point of their art in their education & very often acquire it when they come to Practice at the expense of their patients' safety. . . .

I am Dear Sir Your most affectionate & Dutyfull Son,

Joseph Black

HENDRICK VAN BEUREN (born 1725)

In the spring of 1754 there appeared in the *New York Gazette* or the *Weekly Post Boy* the following anonymous letter:

Flatbush, May 20, 1754

Mr. Printers:—

giving a place in one of your papers to the underwritten will oblige yours

Dr. Hendrick.

The daily and unnumerable abuses that are committed on the bodies of our Fellow Creatures, in the practice of Physic and Surgery by the unskilful practitioners to both: and the deplorable instances of Havock and Devastation occasioned by such Intestine Enemies (destructive to any State as a raging pestilence) is obvious to all men of Judgment and Observation.

How solicitous ought every Monarchy and Commonwealth to be about the Health and Preservation of every Individual. The ancient Romans were very singular in this way. Anyone who had the good fortune to save the life of any Roman Citizen was dignified with an Oaken Garland. Even the diminutive Republic of St. Marina (sic.) in Italy, in our days is very remarkable for their judicious choice in a Physician under whose hands the Common Wealth thrives. A proper regulation in this respect, so necessary in this province, will be likely never to take place without the Attention and Concurrence of the Legislature.

Every pitiful Fellow, now a Days, (more dexterous at murdering or maiming his Patient than at Terms of Art) assumes to himself, with no small Arrogance, the Appelation of Doctor: far from being due to Quacks and Medicasters and only due to Gentlemen of the Faculty, the undoubted Sons of Aesculapius. So venerable a Distinction is become rather a Term of Reproach to those to whom it particularly belongs; who have taken the highest degree in that Art of Science in some University; or at least ought to be qualified for so doing.

Well may a Gentleman of the Faculty in the City of New York particularly distinguished for his uncommon merit, disdain the Apellation when he must share it with Numbers who can have no pretention to it at all; and even with Apothecaries Apprentices before they have finished their elaborate studies and Applications for three long years. . . .

Obviously the writer, Dr. Hendrick van Beuren, was exasperated. Himself undoubtedly qualified to use the title of "Doctor," he had to share this distinction with many others who had no claim to it. Only few American physicians, who had graduated from European universities, were legitimate "M.D.'s"; all others were "Doctor" by courtesy only.

But worse than the usurpation of a title by practitioners with "no pretention to it at all" was the quality of the medicine they practiced. Harsh words did the doctor use about it, but hardly less harsh were those of vitriolic Dr. William Douglass. "In general," wrote Douglass, "the physical practice in our colonies is so perniciously bad, that excepting in surgery, and some very acute cases, it is better to let nature, under a proper regimen, take her course, than to trust to the honesty and sagacity of the

JOHN BARD (1716-1799)

During the major part of the eighteenth century, medical education in America was on a low plane. It consisted usually in being apprenticed to an older practitioner who, too, had had no formal training. With the founding of medical schools in Philadelphia (in 1765), New York (in 1767) and Cambridge (in 1782), conditions improved; only slowly, however, since the schools were small and their caliber not very high. American physicians desirous of receiving good medical training found it necessary to go to Europe—a custom which prevailed well into the beginning of the present century.

Dr. John Bard, a well-known New York practitioner, had the ambition of affording his young son Samuel a better medical education than he himself had received. Young Bard went abroad in 1762, at considerable expense to his father, and spent three years at the medical school in Edinburgh and in the hospitals in London. The correspondence between father and son, carried out at regular intervals, gives a good picture of medical problems and personalities of the mid-eighteenth century.

The following two letters from the elder Bard to his son were written shortly before the latter's return to America.

To his son Samuel

New York, Jan. 13, 1765

. . . I advise you to cultivate, while in London, the acquaintance of Drs. Huck, Franklin, Fothergill, West, &c. which will naturally lead you into company necessary, after a severe college life, to give you that polite easy carriage, which of all things most commends a gentleman, and which is only to be acquired in company of good taste, and the want of which is a great injury to the three young men already arrived. You have always had an easy temper and manner adapted to make friends: the grafting upon these, a polite, affable, and cheerful behaviour, is not difficult; although sometimes the air of a college is not so readily worn off. Where the physician and gentleman unite, you never perceive any thing of pedantry; it argues both ignorance and vanity—not ignorance perhaps of the profession, but of every thing else. A physician should never assume that, but at his patient's bed-side, and even then, avoid all formality.

My dear son, pardon one piece of advice more; a gentleman always appears to great advantage in his private letters. There is no fault to be found with the sentiments or style of yours, but I wish you would endeavour to be a little neater, in their external form and dress. It is an accomplishment by no means below a gentleman: there is a gentility even in the manner of folding and sealing, and I am the more particular on this occasion, as I know nothing you are remiss in, excepting this point which you think more trifling than I do.

Mr. Kempe wishes I could supply you with five hundred pounds sterling, as he says he is convinced of your abilities and merit in your profession, and nothing should be spared to make you return a finished gentleman, as well as a good physician. In answer to this, I have told him, that it is the man, and not the expense, that forms that character. Good sense, goodness of heart, and a manner that is wholly a man's own, and arises from these qualifications, with the advantages of good company, will ever form the gentleman, and an exceeding agreeable character.

To his son Samuel

New York, Feb. 19, 1765

I very much approve of your first visiting Holland and France, before you go to London, and then to prosecute the scheme you mention of attending to the mode of prescribing, of the most eminent physicians. A neat and simple manner of prescribing, is a great proof of a physician's skill, and greatly conducive to the patient's safety. . . . As the time is now not far off when I expect the happiness of seeing you, permit me to mention one thing which, perhaps, is needless. In your taste of clothes preserve a plain and manly fashion, as well as in your manners. I know many young men of learning and talents, so captivated by this feather, as greatly to lessen that esteem they would otherwise obtain. Be extremely neat, but plain in your dress, set off by an easy, cheerful, open, candid address, and joined with such a becoming gravity as arises from the mind being engaged on subjects of importance. Consider further, my dear son, that New York is to be the place of your residence, where plainness in dress has been long the taste of men of the greatest fortune, and much respect is due to the fashion and custom of the country where you live.

WILLIAM CULLEN (1712-1790)

William Cullen, professor at the Edinburgh Medical School, was for many years the foremost British teacher of medicine. His lectures, which were renowned for their clearness, enjoyed great popularity and were, in contrast to the prevailing custom, delivered in English instead of Latin. His students, in whom he took great personal interest, were strongly attached to him and often remained so for life. Cullen had many engaging characteristics of which not the least was what one of his biographers called a "noble carelessness" about money.

After leaving Edinburgh, many of his former students, who came from all parts of Great Britain and her Colonies, remained in communication with him. To one of them, Dr. Matthew Dobson, of Liverpool, England, Cullen sent the following letter:

To Matthew Dobson, M.D.

Undated (written after 1776)

I think myself much obliged to you for the communication of your experiments (on the Urine in Diabetes), and you do me a great deal of honour in asking my opinion of them. A little indisposition has given me some leisure to consider them, and I give you my judgement with all the candour and freedom which friendship ought to beget.

I must say, in the first place, that I think you have made a discovery. Many have taken notice of the sweet taste of the urine in diabetes, and though there are cases, as I know certainly, in which it does not occur, it was very wrong in any body to deny it altogether, and though, in spite of such assertions, there was little doubt of the fact, yet you have done something in putting it beyond all doubt by your experiments. This, however, is little, and you have done much more by shewing that a saccharine matter is present in considerable quantity, that such a matter is present in the serum, and therefore it must arise from a defect in the assimilating power of sanguification, if I may so speak. I think you judge properly in asserting that sugar is in some cases produced in the animal economy; but the origin of the sugar that appears, it is not necessary to explain, and it is enough for you to shew, that the saccharine matter introduced may subsist in that state longer than has been thought, and may give occasion to phenomena, the cause of which it was otherwise very difficult to assign. All this must throw light on the diabetes, and may probably suggest methods of cure more certain than those hitherto pursued, and the public must consider themselves as obliged to you for putting them in the proper train of investigation. . . .

Dr. Cullen was right. Dobson's work indeed "threw light" on diabetes and it did suggest "methods of cure," but a century and a half had to elapse before, with the discovery of insulin, it became possible to control this disease effectively.

WILLIAM HUNTER (1718-1783)

The announcements of new "cures" for cancer have long become perennial occurrences. Hailed frequently with great enthusiasm, and little critical judgment, they have all been relegated to limbo. Two hundred years ago, the famous van Swieten, the physician and protégé of Empress Maria Theresia, was "curing" cancer in Vienna with an extract made from cicuta (hemlock). In London, Dr. William Hunter, a man of great reputation, tested van Swieten's method. This is what he had to tell his friend Dr. Cullen about it:

To William Cullen, M.D.

February 10, 1761

. . . The Cicuta has done nothing in London, yet the accounts from Vienna, particularly from Van Swieten, rise higher every day. It is suspected that our extract was made too late in the season, or that the plant in this climate is not rich or powerful, but my own suspicions are quite of another kind. We shall in time know how it is, but I am afraid we shall have no cure for a Cancer. . . .

London at this period was an important medical center. It had no medical school but a number of good hospitals and many brilliant physicians among whom the Hunter brothers, John and William, were especially outstanding. William Hunter, the writer of the foregoing letter and of the following one, was a renowned teacher of anatomy, a leading obstetrician and a competent medical practitioner. His treatment of what must have been a serious febrile disease is described in this letter to a patient's father:

To a patient's father

Newport, June 4th, 1774

When I first saw your son, his Fever being then high, I was in hopes that it might be rapid enough to exhaust itself in 9, 11, or 15 days, but since it has become so low as to continue from 80 to 106, the period of it becomes more uncertain. . . . In this Fever *Wine* is the medicine that must be depended upon. Good Wine possesses all the virtues of the Cordial medicines, while it is free from many of their bad qualitys. I say good Wine; for however common this article of Luxury is now become, it is rarely to be obtained genuine. Mustard Whey will be a very proper Drink for your son which give him freely for his common drink.

Mustard Whey is made by boiling two or three Table Spoonfulls of powdered Mustard in an English pint of Milk mixed with an equal quantity of water. After it has boiled some time a Gill of good Old Madeira may be added to it. . . . In a word, the great aim in this disease is to support the patient's spirits, by giving him frequently small quantitys of the above, or other drinks of a warm and cordial nature. He is not however to be over heated either with Liquor or clothes. . . . The free use of good Wine and Blistering are the only things to be depended on in this kind of Fever. If he shou'd be delirious, he ought to be blistered on the Neck, and it will be the Safest course, while the Fever continues, as soon as the discharge occasioned by one blister abates, to apply another somewhere else, and by that means keep up a continual succession of them untill he is out of danger. . . . When the Fever continues after the 22d day you must expect no sensible Crices only his Fever and Symptoms will leave him very slowly and insensibly go off, which that they may do is the sincere desire of Dear Sir

Your very Humble Servant

Wm. Hunter

P.S. Let me hear from you again on Monday, and keep on your Journal for that is very satisfactory. Be very particular to observe every symptom or alteration that may happen to him.—Wrote in much haste.

JOHN FOTHERGILL (1712-1780)

John Fothergill, an early graduate of the famous Edinburgh medical school, was for many years a leading physician in London. An adherent of what today would be called conservative therapy, he eschewed the greater part of the heroic measures so popular in his day. Instead of repeated and copious bleeding, sweating, blistering, purging and the uninhibited use of drastic medicines, Fothergill resorted to bland diets, rest, mild-acting drugs. His knowledge, his personality and the novelty of his therapeutic approach soon made him one of the most popular physicians. His reputation was great, his practice extensive and his life very strenuous.

To Dr. Johnstone

London, March 24, 1762

If my leisure was equal to my inclination, Dr. Johnstone would not have been so long without some intimations of the regard and esteem I have for him. But I live an exile in the midst of a most populous city, and secluded from all correspondence in the centre of it. It is only at night that I can have a moment's respite, and even seldom then: and judge with what reluctance one sits down to write even to a friend, when every faculty of body and mind has been kept upon full stretch for twelve or fourteen hours together: and this is my case daily, with a body not strong, and a mind not a little actuated with feelings for those I serve.

... Should I live to enjoy a few years of respite from excessive labour, before my faculties, such as they are, are quite worn out, I should be glad to leave behind me a few way marks to posterity; not that I have made any discoveries, except it be of a few bogs and precipices, where an inattentive traveller may perhaps, from any thing yet left us that I know of, be liable to miss his way, and suffer for it.—Has any body ever thought of writing Le Medicin de *bon Sens?* yet what is more wanting in the practice of physic?—the means of acquiring that superiority with their patients, that commands their punctual obedience. —It is a science worth studying, hard to be learned, as hard to be taught, yet of some consequence. I am not the person who can do it, but I could wish to attempt it. Excuse this prolixity, and believe me to be thy assured friend. . . .

Two letters from Fothergill on behalf of patients give a good picture of his medical thinking. The first letter contains advice for a tuberculous patient, the second discusses the regimen for a patient with gout.

To Dr. Johnstone

London, April 25, 1759

Yesterday I received thy obliging letter, and the case it inclosed. I have considered this with attention; and sit down to give my opinion, though with much doubt of any thing availing, as well as my present situation will allow.

I am afraid a *Phthisis* is so far confirmed, that nothing can retard a gradual but certain dissolution of the whole. I know of nothing, at least under such circumstances, that promises so much as the Bristol water, drank at the Wells. . . .

... His diet should be much of the milky kind, and of the lightest animal food, a little at once, and the oftener repeated; his exercise very moderate; and the slightest cold studiously avoided. In regard to medicine, after the trial of so many efficacious ones, it is difficult to propose any with a prospect of much success. The remedies proposed on the paper within, may, with such variations as Dr. Johnstone sees necessary, be worth a trial. The intention at present seems, to mitigate the cough, without totally stopping expectoration; and to lessen the inflammatory tendency, without weakening the vis vitae. Every thing in medicine, as well as diet, of an active, heating, stimulating nature, should be studiously avoided: the mildest balsamics, with a gentle astringency intermixed, with antiseptics and anodynes, are all that seem at present indicated. ...

To John C. Lettsom, M.D.

October 21, 1778

... To a man of quick sensations, to acquire an absolute command over appetite, requires more philosophy, more strength of mind, than most people are aware of. Yet it is the want of this command, and too easily yielding to the present moment of appetite, that not only disposes constitutions that are even averse to gout, to feel all its miseries; but precipitates those who are entitled to it by birth, and, I may say, education, to the full severity of its torture. —If our friend can resolve to restrain himself, he may add to his days many years; if not, the whole that art can do, is to extricate him from the effects of inattention, as long as nature assists us. It is much to be wished, that gouty persons could be prevailed on to fall on some plan to correct this propensity, and that they would never dine upon more than one dish at a time; and, if there is much variety on the table, to chuse *that* which they *like* the least. Therefore say to our friend, If he regards his own life, the happiness of his family, his friends, and his country, he must either now determine to conform to the strictest regimen, agreeable to the rules here suggested, or prepare himself for the miserable life of an invalid—either extreme pain, or unutterable dejection of spirits; according to what I have observed in a thousand similar instances.

During his earlier years in London, Fothergill was the physician of a young lady to whom he was very much attached. A charming letter of advice to her shows how kind a man and solicitous a physician he was.

To a young patient

(Written about 1749)

Though I have ever placed thee in the rank of those whom I think it an honour to be permitted to attend in the way of my profession, yet I am never sent for upon thy account but it gives me some pain, both as I cannot forbear pitying the distressed, and as in thy case more especially I am concerned lest the present indisposition should lay the foundation of any other whose consequences might be more threatening. . . .

It would be tedious to both to give a great many rules with regard to diet. The stomach is in general the best director; what ever it takes with pleasure, I mean with regard to quality, is always preferable to any other; but to regulate the quantity is not always easy; yet to leave off rather short is sometimes necessary, even though the appetite seems yet lively. Nothing tends more to keep off heaviness, feverish heats, or lowness of spirits,

than a care in this one point. I know it is objected, that to
hinder persons who eat but very little from eating as much as
they can is unreasonable. But experience is on my side, and I
will appeal to every prudent person who has tried the effect of
eating slowly, and sometimes with a little restraint.

This abstemious method has likewise another good effect; it
allows a glass of wine to be drunk without injury; nay it renders
it necessary and beneficial. I am certain that under such circumstances a glass or two of good red wine would be of great use to
thyself.

I think butter, fat meats, or anything much seasoned will not
be agreeable, I mean so as to make them a considerable part of
thy diet. The first are relaxing, the last heats the blood too much.
I do not say that butter is absolutely to be avoided; only that
it is not quite so inoffensive in habits like thine as some think.
When it is quite fresh and new it is the least detrimental.

As I have frequently mentioned my opinion of tea I shall say
little of it now: only permit me to add that I am no enemy to it
from prejudice, but from experiment: I like it too well myself
not to wish that I might allow every one to drink it without
restraint. But it certainly relaxes the stomach, in time weakens
the digestion, and infallibly renders the constitution itself more
delicate, tender and weakly than it is by nature. Strong and
healthy people, who drink freely, are so far from feeling any ill
effects from its use that it is often advantageous to them, but
we are neither of us of this rank: if we must therefore drink
tea let it be in small quantities, not hot, not immoderately
strong.

Let me prevail upon thee never to read immediately after
dinner, and after supper not too much. It is next to impossible,
if the subject is at all interesting, entirely to forget it, when it is
necessary to seek repose. The nature of my employment has for
a long time engaged me in a contrary conduct, and I have suf-

fered accordingly, yet almost without a power of altering it. What necessary study began choice soon induced me to continue, and a strong desire of being behind nobody in the faculty, as far as industry, capacity and opportunities of improvement would suffer me. I only mention these to assure thee the more strongly, that reading at nights with any attention or concern about what we read is highly prejudicial to health.

When I have had resolution enough to throw aside my book or my pen for the latter part of the evening, and only entertained myself with reviewing the actions of the day, I have thought it the most agreeable way of spending half an hour before I go to bed. Not that my conduct is always such that it merits my own approbation; far from it, but [rather] the pleasing hope of its being a likely method of growing wiser and better, and of drawing down the favourable regard of an infinitely good and benevolent Protector by a silent appeal to his awful majesty. Thus committing ourselves to his care, we become tranquil and serene; our repose is undisturbed, the blood flows with ease, the motion of the spirits is calm and regular, we awake refreshed, without feverish heats, headaches, thirst, or any of those other consequences of interrupted rest and restrained perspiration.

Exercise we have frequently had occasion to mention, and I dare not enter upon it here, because I should not be able to say enough, or must say too little. In general that exercise is the most healthful in which the mind takes most part. Travelling is of this sort, and that I have often or more than once recommended.

But I must not omit to make some observations upon dress. I own that with a less impartial person than myself whatever I might say on this subject would be little regarded, as I discover in my own [attire] what many will naturally look upon as either prejudice or want of taste. But I will endeavour to convince thee that what I shall say upon this head arises less from my particular sentiments about some parts of the dress of your sex than from a just enquiry and consideration of it.

I am mistaken if the first part which I would mention is not already sufficiently attended to, yet a caution can do no prejudice. I mean an absolute freedom and ease in that part of your sex's dress which is frequently the most nicely contrived for injuring the health; not the hoop but the stays. Whilst they support the body with ease, and without closely confining any particular part, they are useful. But if they press upon the stomach, straiten the breast, or imprison the waist, they are the most certainly pernicious of anything that the art of man could have invented in the nature of dress. Nay, it must have been a contrivance of some of your sex; ours love you too well to have been originally guilty of such cruelty. In short, if the stays are not perfectly easy, they must, they will be injurious, and I intreat thee, by all the regard thou owes to a most affectionate father, to be just to thyself and to him in this respect. I readily acknowledge that I have no reason in particular for saying this, but I mention it as a caution in general. . . .

JOHN COAKLEY LETTSOM (1744-1815)

John Coakley Lettsom was probably the most popular London physician between the 1780's and the 1810's. Born in the Virgin Islands in 1744 he was sent to England at the age of six to be educated at a Friends school. Later he was apprenticed to a surgeon and apothecary in Yorkshire from where he went to London to continue his medical training. However, his means were so limited that he had to interrupt his studies and return to the West Indies, where he soon had a flourishing practice. Relinquishing it after a short time and utilizing its proceeds for further study he was finally able to establish himself in London.

He made no original contribution to medicine but he was distinguished as a physician of great common sense. His name became associated with charitable and social movements: medical care for the poor, establishment of dispensaries, prison reform. His largess was virtually unlimited and a major part of his great earnings was expended for charitable purposes.

An enthusiastic physician and indefatigable worker, he often saw, as he once wrote, "a hundred to a hundred and fifty patients before breakfast." Truly, the practice of medicine was no sinecure, but it was fulfillment to him.

To a friend

London, Sept. 6, 1791

Knowing, as I do, the difficulties attendant on the medical profession, I confess I feel a reluctance in recommending the pursuit of it; and yet I can say, were I to commence life anew, I know of no profession, arduous as it is, that I should so cordially embrace. The delay in acquiring employment, and the solicitude attending it, especially from the fatality which shades the best exertions of skill, may be urged against it; but I think a humane physician, who evinces by his conduct a tender interest in the recovery of his patient, never loses reputation by an event which no human means could prevent; on the contrary, oftentimes nearer attachments are acquired; for the sympathy of the physician makes him appear almost as one of the family, and mutual anxiety begets mutual endearment. This I have felt and seen daily, and sometimes the pleasure of rational melancholy, if I may so term it, are the most permanent, and the most consolatory to a feeling heart. On the other hand, when health follows skill, what pleasures result! Well might it be said by Cicero, "Nothing brings men nearer the gods than by giving health to their fellow creatures." You are a guardian angel of the family, and a deity of health, and the sensations of your own breast are inexpressibly delightful. But it is not a lucrative profession. It is a divine one. It is above money, and is "not to be dealt in by attorneyship," as Shakespeare says of Love. . . . Remember me to the partner of thy bed, and the young shoots; and believe me

Thine, respectfully,

To a physician friend

Sept. 3, 1795

. . . medicine . . . is the highest and most divine profession, that can engage human intellect. I have attended eighty-two thousand patients, and what can equal the dignity of having so many lives intrusted to your decision!—What more divine, than to soothe the afflicted, and soften agony! What more sublime than to restore to life the victim of disease! I envy not the prince on the throne, nor the sultan in his haram, whilst I enjoy the confidence of the sick chamber, and the blessings of the restored. I love my profession, perhaps too much. It loves me, and I have no objection to die in the chamber of malady, provided I can mitigate it in a fellow creature,—and so every other physician would, I doubt not, reason. . . .

To a medical correspondent who, deploring the seamy side of a medical man's life, had often "been on the point of abjuring the practice of physic," Lettsom wrote:

To W. Cuming, M.D.

Feb. 18, 1783

. . . I did not expect I should ever have occasion to differ in sentiment from Dr. Cuming; but with respect to all those dreadful pictures he has so painfully exhibited of the *impuissance* of our art, I feel, I mean I have experienced, very different impressions. A physician is always supposed to have formed a judicious prognostic, to have foreseen *"the convulsive pangs of an expiring husband and father,"* and all the subsequent catalogue of distresses; but here, my friend, it is, that, when in the physician, the friend and the divine are combined, his affection, his good sense, and his sympathy, pours into the afflicted the oil of comfort; he soothes the pangs of woe; he mitigates the distress; he finds out something in the wise dispensations of Providence that he carries home to the bosom of affliction. Here it is that he is truly a guardian angel. . . . he is become the father of the family —he is everything that Heaven in kindness deputes, to soften, to dissipate misery. I declare, a conscientious physician in the midst of his solicitude, experiences here that melancholy joy, that permanent ecstacy, which is annexed to the desire of doing good. I have felt the tenderest springs of friendship in such an attitude. . . .

Medical knowledge in Lettsom's age was primitive and fragmentary, and many of its practices were but poorly understood. An example of what physicians believed to be a permissible procedure is described in the following letter written by Dr. Lettsom in 1785:

Sept. 15, 1785

. . . Either our vices, or humanity itself, has accumulated a sufficient number of maladies upon flesh and blood. Within a few years a new one has appeared. About nine of these cases have occurred in as many years. Two were fatal. It arises from the transplanting of fresh or live human teeth. The person who receives them, for a month or two appears well, the teeth become as firm as can be. Then comes on gradually an ulceration of the maxilla, to which succeeds a general eruption of the skin, like unto that termed syphilitic. In about twenty days from the commencement of the ulceration of the maxilla, the throat also ulcerates, and nodes appear on the legs. All these symptoms look like syphilis, but the disease is cured by bark without mercury, and the patients from whom the teeth have been taken, have been, I believe, virgins, or, at least, perfectly healthy. . . .

And as late as 1812 a physician as experienced as Lettsom could still look upon tuberculosis as a disease "not usually deemed infectious."

To a physician

April 22, 1812

... With respect to the digitalis in pulmonary consumptions, I believe it never cured one, and that its indiscriminate use has killed many; I would not, however, totally discard it; the qualities of lessening the impetus of the circulation, and the quickness of the pulse, are not trivial, if well directed; but, alas! what single remedy can avail in this *malevolent* disease, which, in a peculiar manner, preys upon youth and beauty. Foreigners had long noticed the frequency of this disease in London; and rather more than 40 years ago, the faculty of Paris addressed the college here, to learn from it, whether or not this malady resulted from the use of coal fires. Dr. Fothergill told me that it was answered in the negative, as consumptions were as frequent in those parts of England where peat, turf, or wood, were the usual fuel. Since this period consumptions are spread over the continent, and perhaps the disease is full as frequent in Paris and Vienna, as in London, and lately still more frequent in America, particularly in New York and Philadelphia. My friend Dr. Anthony Fothergill, now in the latter city, has sent me the bills of mortality in these Trans-Atlantic cities, and I find the proportion of deaths, by consumptions, are in both truly alarming. Is this extension of a disease, not usually deemed infectious, to be ascribed to a change of habit; and the revolution in light clothing? ...

Lettsom's manifold activities brought him into contact with many of the prominent people of his day. A letter to James Boswell, one of the "social lions" in London, throws an interesting light on both men.

To James Boswell

June 18, 1791

When I acknowledge that ever since I had the pleasure of thy acquaintance I have felt a singular esteem for thee, I only express a sentiment which every other person must feel if placed in the same situation. The generosity, the candour, the openness of thy heart, combine to acquire and to secure the attachment of every liberal mind. This attachment I presume to claim; it is this that compels me to risk thy future friendship, by embracing the freedom which it inspires.

I have, my friend, had some occasions of viewing thee in the most interesting situations, when thy whole soul has been poured out in social enjoyment, I might have said extacy, and in no point of view canst thou appear more endearing; for those will love thee most who see most of thy heart. But in these scenes of pleasure, which I have cordially enjoyed, sometimes a sigh of solicitude has burst upon me, lest by any unguarded excitement of such conviviality a bodily constitution may be undermined, and that life thereby shortened, which every man of refinement and virtuous sociality must wish long, very long preserved.

I have observed, not merely a too frequent use of the glass, but that mixture of liquors which, as a professional man, I can add, tends to injure the best human fabrick. I will add further, what ample experience authorizes, that by whatever means the spirits are exhilarated beyond the chaste medium of nature, the alternation of mental languor will result; so that the depression is great in proportion to the degree of foreign excitement.

Two motives embolden me thus to recall sober reflection, to chasten and to moderate the fascinating influence of social pleasures, either too frequently repeated or too far extended. I feel in the first place the emotions of friendship, which I cannot repress; and in the next, the intrinsic solid sense of one I am proud to call my friend: these equally impel me to risk his censure, whilst the latter encourages me to subscribe myself his sincerely.

WILLIAM FALCONER (1744-1824)

Quacks and charlatans have always found willing dupes. Especially among those seeking relief from real, and often not so real, illnesses. Ranging all the way from petty rogues to big-scale impostors, they have often exercised great influence over their admiring followers. Nowhere are their activities possibly more damaging than in the field of medical care and from nowhere are they more difficult to dislodge.

Why so many persons, and they are often by no means simpletons, should turn to all forms of medical quackery has found many, more or less satisfactory, explanations. The following views of a physician who lived two hundred years ago contain much food for thought.

To John Coakley Lettsom, M.D.

Oct. 21, 1776

... I am highly pleased with your pamphlet on that audacious impostor Mayersbach. The measure of credulity will be never full, nor does, in this instance, one generation improve by the experience of the last. What an imposition this to be practised in the 18th century, when we are all so eager to cast off all imposition both in arts, politics, and religion! It will remain as a monument of the folly of the nation in our history, and make posterity discredit our accounts of the improvements made in this age. I am sure, however, Dr. Lettsom deserves the thanks and gratitude of the public in a high degree, for his disinterested and brave attempt to undeceive a foolish people. I fear however, the faculty are, in some measure, the causes themselves. That air of mystery they assume, and the little care they take of their own improvement when past the trammels of a school and college, which the world easily see, as well as several other faults, make such deceits as Mayersbach's more easily swallowed.

JAMES CURRIE (1756-1805)

At the age of fifteen, much against the wish of his father, who had wanted him to be a physician, James Currie emigrated to Virginia with the intention of becoming a businessman. Finding life in the Colonies not congenial, he returned, like many another man, to the mother country and took up medicine. A man of many interests, especially philosophical and literary (after Robert Burns's death he edited the poet's works), he occupied himself also with transcendental philosophy, a predilection which may account for the trend of mind described in the following letter.

Although the old adage "there is nothing new under the sun" is certainly no longer correct, it still has a good deal of validity. As, for instance, in respect to the "newness" of psychosomatic concepts.

To George Bell, M.D.

October 20, 1781

I begin to find that, notwithstanding all my engagements, I have some time left for study, and I have formed a resolution to employ it (if possible) in some way that may contribute to my present happiness and my future fame. There is a part of the philosophy of medicine that has as yet been little attended to; I mean that which treats of the diseases of the mind, of the influence of affections primarily mental, on the corporeal functions, and particularly of the passions and emotions. Something,

I am convinced, might be done on this subject. Every author whom I have read, in treating on it, has immediately exclaimed on its great difficulty, and most of them have asserted that it is impossible that we should ever acquire any knowledge on a business so intricate. But though we may never know *how* mind acts on matter, we may, by a careful attention, possibly discover the general principles of this action; which is all, indeed, that we are able to attain in regard to the action of matter on matter. If I ever do any thing to be remembered, it must be on some such subject, for I am utterly unfit for those studies which are at present so fashionable. I despise the pitiful matter-of-fact knowledge, which is busy with the wings of butterflies and phials of mutton broth; and my contempt is mixed with indignation, when I consider the arrogance and self-conceit to which such employments give birth. But the mind of man is, in my eye, a noble field for speculation. By self-contemplation the intellectual faculties are strengthened, the conceptions are enlarged, the sentiments ennobled, and the soul is prepared for that state where its chief employment is said to be the contemplation of that Being, of which it is the emanation. If you are alone when this meets your eye, and disposed for thought, you will conceive the sensations with which it is written; but if you should be in the coffee-room playing with such fellows as —— and —— at a guinea a point, you will think it mere rant and bombast.

In regard to myself, I have not much to say! —I get a little practice, but my patients seem to die out of spite. . . .

WILLIAM HEBERDEN (1710-1801)

The training of the medical student has at all times been of great concern to physicians. Its forms necessarily depended in great measure on the status of medicine itself. When medicine was more or less a craft, apprenticeship was the usual form of instruction; as it progressed to be a science, academic training came to the fore; finally, a synthesis had to be found between the purely practical instruction of the apprentice and the more theoretical training of the university student.

Writing to a medical friend toward the end of the eighteenth century, Dr. William Heberden, one of the most eminent English physicians of his day, took the following optimistic stand:

To Thomas Percival, M.D.

Pall-Mall, Oct. 15, 1794

. . . There has lately been established in several of the London hospitals, a plan of courses of lectures in all the branches of knowledge useful to a student of physic. Such plans, if rightly executed, as I have no reason to doubt they will be, must make London a school of physic superior to most in Europe. The experience afforded in an hospital will keep down the luxuriance of plausible theories. Many such have been delivered in lectures, by celebrated teachers, with great applause; but the students, though perfectly masters of them, not having corrected them with what nature exhibits in an hospital, have found themselves more at a loss in the cure of a patient than an elder apprentice of an apothecary. I please myself with thinking that the method of teaching the art of healing is becoming every day more conformable to what reason and nature require; that the errors introduced by superstition and false philosophy are gradually retreating; and that medical knowledge, as well as all other dependent upon observation and experience, is continually increasing in the world. The present race of physicians are possessed of several most important rules of practice, utterly unknown to the ablest in former ages, not excepting Hippocrates himself, or even Aesculapius.

JOHN WARREN (1753-1815)

Conditions in the American Army Hospitals during the War of the Revolution were appalling. The following appeal by a young military surgeon, Dr. John Warren, for food and medical supplies for his patients gives a vivid picture of their distressing situation.

[1778]

To His Excellency the Governor and Honorable the Council of the Commonwealth of Massachusetts

Though I have frequently represented the distressed condition of the sick in the Continental Hospital, yet I have never had so ample occasion to deplore their miseries as at present.

For some days they have not had an ounce of meat; not a stick of wood but what they have taken from the neighboring fences; for near a week not a vegetable; and scarcely any medicine for above a year. In fine, to sum up the whole in a few words, the sick and wounded, many of which are exceedingly dangerous, and some of them in a state which requires immediate amputation, are not furnished by the public with a single article of sustenance except bread alone, and must have perished ere this had not the charitable donations of a few individuals in some measure contributed to their relief.

I have been incessantly making application for these last twelve months to all the departments for supplies, but cannot procure any. During which time the groans of the sick and wounded, suffering, and perhaps dying, for want of necessities, have been perpetually saluting my ears. I must, therefore, beg your Excellency and Honors' action in this matter, and am with the greatest respect, gentlemen,

Your most obedient servant,
J. Warren.

After the war John Warren settled in Boston. Although he had had no academic medical training and was a doctor "by courtesy" only, he became one of the town's leading physicians and, in 1782, the first Professor of Anatomy and Surgery at the newly-founded Harvard Medical College, an institution which could boast of a total of three professors.

The dearth of scientific and artistic activities in the United States at the close of the eighteenth century was keenly felt by some Americans. A letter written by Dr. Warren in 1790 to Dr. John Lettsom in London is an interesting expression of their sentiments.

To John C. Lettsom, M.D.

Boston, May 30, 1790

. . . By the direction of the Massachusetts Medical Society, I have, as their corresponding Secretary, presented you with a copy of papers communicated to them, and selected for publication; and I herewith send you another, as a small acknowledgement for the favours of this kind, which I have received from you. The poverty of this country, with respect to literary productions, is such, that I am not enabled, by any means, to make that return which your notices to me in this way, merit. We are, however, making some advances, I trust, in the paths of science, and we shall think it no dishonour to imitate the means by which the enlightened nations of Europe, and particularly England, have become so celebrated for their cultivation of the arts. At a humble distance, we shall indeed long remain, but from the labours of the industrious, something advantageous may, in all countries, be derived. An intercourse with the learned, on your side the Atlantic, will greatly aid our efforts, and stimulate to a laudable exertion in the pursuit.

BENJAMIN RUSH (1746-1813)

In midsummer, 1793, the inhabitants of Philadelphia, then the largest city in the United States, were greatly alarmed by the occurrence of yellow fever, a disease at that period endemic in America. At first localized, it soon spread throughout the city. The following excerpts from the letters of Dr. Benjamin Rush to his wife who, like many others, had left the stricken city with her children, give an idea of the dreadful course of the epidemic.

To his wife

Aug. 25, 1793

Since my letter to you of Friday, the fever has assumed a most alarming appearance. It not only mocks in most instances the power of medicine, but it has spread thro' several parts of the city remote from the spot where it originated. Water Street between Arch and Race Streets is nearly desolated by it. This morning I witnessed a scene there, which reminded me of the histories I had read of the plague. In one house I lost two patients last night, a respectable young merchant and his only child. His wife is frantic this evening with grief. Five other persons died in the neighbourhood yesterday afternoon and four more last night at Kensington. . . .

Aug. 29, 1793

. . . The disease has raged with great virulence this day. Among the dead are Woodruf Sims, and Mr. Stiles the stone cutter. The last exhibited signs of the plague before he died. I have seen the same symptoms in the hospital fever during the late war. They have however greatly increased the terror of our citizens, and have excited an apprehension that it is in reality the Plague, but this I am sure is not the case, altho' it comes nearer to it in violence and mortality than any disease we have ever before had in this country. Its symptoms are very different in different people. Sometimes it comes on with a chilly fit, and a high fever, but more frequently it steals on with headache, languor and sick stomach. These symptoms are followed by stupor, delirium, vomiting, a dry skin, cool or cold hands and feet, a feeble slow pulse, sometimes below in frequency the pulse of health. The eyes are at first suffused with blood, they afterwards become yellow, and in most cases a yellowness covers the whole skin on the 3rd. or 4th. day. Few survive the 5th. day, but more die on the 2nd. and 3rd. days. In some cases the patients possess their reason to the last, and discover much less weakness than in the last stage of common fevers. One of my patients stood up and shaved himself on the morning of the day he died. Livid spots on the body, a bleeding at the nose, from the gums and from the bowels, and a vomiting of black matter in some instances close the scenes of life. The common remedies for malignant fevers have all failed. Bark, wine and blisters make no impression upon it. Baths of hot vinegar applied by means of blankets, and the cold bath have relieved and saved some. . . .

Sept. 18, 1793

. . . But this is only the background of the distress which pervades our city. Many die without nurses. Some perish from the want of a draught of water. Parents desert their children as soon as they are infected, and in every room you enter, you see no person but a solitary black man or woman near the sick. Many people thrust their parents into the streets, as soon as they complain of a headache. . . .

Oct. 23, 1793

I am sorry to inform you that the late moderate weather has so far revived the disease, that the mortality is nearly as great as before the late rain and cold weather. 700 have died since the 11 of October. 3400 have died since the first of August. O! that God would hear the cries and groans of the many hundred, and perhaps thousand sick which still ascend to his throne every hour of the day and night, from our desolating city! I feel the distress of my fellow citizens the more from my being unable to assist them, and from my hearing constantly of some of them being murdered by large and ill-timed doses of bark and wine. But I must not arraign the conduct of divine providence,

> "When obedient nature knows his will,
> A doctor or disease alike can kill."

But when Rush deplores that many of the sick had been "murdered by large and ill-timed doses of bark and wine," it may be well to consider what the effect of *his* method of treatment—drastic purges and excessive bleedings, to the extent of removing four-fifths of a patient's blood—must have been!

A few months later, at the termination of the epidemic, another physician, Dr. William Thornton, wrote to Dr. Lettsom, in London:

William Thornton to John C. Lettsom, M.D.

Dec. 11, 1793

This has been a long night of silence and death.

The city of Philadelphia has exhibited such a spectacle of mortality as I was never before witness to. The scenes were so

affecting, that I cannot think of describing them; but I have
sent thee a pamphlet which, though ill written, will give thee
a tolerable idea of a great part. I think, however, that the account
is under-rated, at least, two thousand. . . .

. . . I think that more people in this city were carried off by
the very copious bleeding, and violent and repeated purges of
jalap and calomel, than would have died if nothing had been
done.

In all diseases which are inflammatory, in the first instance, it
is the special duty of a physician to guard against the subsequent
debility and dangerous prostration of strength. How improper
then to take away such quantities of blood! . . . I was taken with
every symptom of the fever, and saw, from my sick bed, many
dying in different rooms opposite; but I pursued a more moderate
mode, and got well in about *a week*, though I was reduced, in
one day, to a very low state, by the violence of the fever, vomiting, and headache.

When, as was so frequently the custom in those days, Dr.
Rush had been asked to advise a patient without ever personally
having seen him, he wrote:

To Mr. Walter Stone

Philadelphia, January 5, 1791

After maturely considering your case, I am disposed to believe it to be the hypochondriac disorder. This opinion is
founded not only on its causes and symptoms but on the knowledge I now possess of your family constitution.

The first remedy that I would recommend to you is a total

abstraction from business of all kinds for a few months. Come to Philadelphia and spend the remaining part of the winter with your old acquaintances. Frequent our assemblies, and now and then join in a country dance, but never continue that exercise till you are *fatigued*, for the excess of pleasure is worse than the excess of anything else.

Your diet should consist only of *solid food*. Beef and mutton, also wild fowl, venison, and oysters, will be most proper for you. Broths, tea, coffee, and chocolate should for a while be avoided. Three or four glasses of sherry, madeira, or Lisbon wines should be taken every day, and half a pint or more may be taken once a week at a sitting in agreeable company.

To keep your bowels open, eat constantly with your meat a bread made of equal parts of wheat and Indian meal. If this fails, continue to take some of the opening medicine recommended by Dr. Brown.

Your belly should be frequently rubbed with a dry hand, but in so gentle a manner as to give no pain.

Your feet should be kept warm at all times by means of socks or cork soles in your shoes.

The above prescriptions will be more or less effectual according as they are assisted or not by the society of the ladies. The company of one of them for life, I am satisfied, would do more towards restoring you to perfect health than all the other remedies that have ever been prescribed for you.

With sincere wishes for the happy event, I am, dear sir, your friend and servant,

Benjamin Rush

P. S. I do not think your disease should alarm you. By following *all* the above directions, I think your recovery is as certain as physicians dare to pronounce any events to be that relate to the issue of diseases.

The patient seems to have resented the implication that his illness was possibly due to psychological causes. Whereupon he received the following letter:

To Mr. Walter Stone

Philadelphia, January 30, 1791

Your brother communicated to me that part of your late letter to him which related to your disorder. You have mistaken me if you suppose that I believe any part of your complaints to be *imaginary*. On the contrary, I am sure that your disorder is as much a *bodily* one as the pleurisy or the gout. It is however frequently increased by certain states of the mind, particularly by those which occur from solitude or from the *want* of CARE, a certain portion of which is inseparably connected with the exercise of the domestic affections. It was to awaken these affections and to let loose their gentle and agreeable stimulus upon your body that I recommended the immediate choice of a *partner for life.* You need not be afraid of making her a nurse, for your disorder is seldom met with in married life.

I suspected from your first letter that your complaints were mixed with and aggravated by worms. Your last letter has confirmed that suspicion. From that discovery I derive fresh hopes of your perfect recovery. . . .

A remarkable example of professional solicitude! How the doctor made the "discovery" that Mr. Stone's "complaints were mixed with and aggravated by worms" is difficult to conceive of.

Despite his weaknesses, Benjamin Rush was unquestionably a man of great talents and warmness of heart. Much distressed by the lack of understanding and the brutality with which the insane were treated (one of his own sons was incurably demented), he spent much time in the study of mental disease and in the attempt to improve the lot of the mentally deranged. And still, eighteenth-century medical insight was so imperfect that it was possible for him to devise a method of treatment which must have subjected the patient to severe torture.

To John Redman Coxe, M.D.

September 5, 1810

In attending the maniacal patients in the Pennsylvania Hospital, I have long seen with pain the evils of confining them, when ungovernable, by means of what is called the mad shirt or straight waistcoat. It generally reduces them to a recumbent posture, which never fails to increase their disease. In this state they often lie whole days and nights, and sometimes in a situation which delicacy forbids me to mention. The straight waistcoat moreover renders it impracticable to feel their pulse or to bleed them without taking off the greatest part of it. To obviate these evils and at the same time to retain all the benefits of coercion, I requested, by permission of the sitting managers of the Hospital, Mr. Benjamin Lindall, an ingenious cabinetmaker in this city, to make for the benefit of the maniacal patients a strong armchair, with several appropriate peculiarities as noticed in the drawing which I have herewith sent you for your *Museum.* From its design and effects I have called it a TRANQUILLIZER.

It has the following advantages over the straight waistcoat:

1. It lessens the force of the blood in its determination to the head by opposing its gravity to it; and by keeping the head in a fixed and erect position, it prevents the interruption of the passage of the blood to and from the brain by pressure upon any of its blood vessels.

2. It produces more general muscular inaction and of course acts more powerfully in weakening the force of the blood vessels in every part of the body.

3. It places the patient in a situation in which it is possible, without any difficulty, to apply cold water or ice by means of a bladder to the head, and warm water to the feet at the same time.

4. It enables a physician to feel the pulse and to open a vein without relieving any other part of the body from its confinement but a single arm. It enables him likewise to administer purgative medicines without subjecting the patient to the necessity of being moved from his chair or exposing him afterwards to the fetor of his excretions or to their contact with his body.

5. The body of the patient in this chair, though in a state of coercion, is so perfectly free from pressure that he sometimes falls asleep in it.

6. His position in this chair is less irritating to his temper, and much less offensive to the feelings of his friends, than in a straight waistcoat.

I have hitherto employed this chair only as an auxiliary remedy for the cure of the violent state of madness; but I have no doubt it might be employed with advantage in other diseases in which a recumbent posture of the body has been found to be hurtful, particularly in epilepsy, headache, vertigo, wakefulness and sleepiness, and from too much fullness of the blood vessels of the brain. The back of the chair for such cases might be made to fall back at the pleasure of the patient or to suit the grade of his disease. . . .

During his long life Rush was involved in many professional controversies. Undoubtedly he was often subjected to bitter attacks by his colleagues but he certainly did not hesitate to express his sentiments of them. As an old man he wrote to Dr. David Hosack, the prominent New York physician:

To David Hosack, M.D.

Philadelphia, August 15, 1810

. . . I thank you for the liberal manner in which you have dissented from my opinions upon the subject of your present inquiries. In the laudable attempts which are now making to improve the condition of mankind, I wish a society could be formed to *humanize* physicians. General Lee once said, "Oh! that I were a dog, that I might not call man a brother!" With how much more reason might I say, "Oh! that I were a member of any other profession than that of medicine, that I might not call physicians my brethren!"

And a year before his death he had these bitter words to say about medical men:

To the same

June 20, 1812

Our Philosophical Society meets but once a month in summer. They met last evening. Their next meeting will be on the *third* Friday of next month, which is, I think, on the 17th of the month, on which day, or before it, I shall expect to have the pleasure of taking you by the hand as my guest. All my family unite with me in requesting you to make our house your home while you remain in Philadelphia. Let us show the world that a difference of opinion upon medical subjects is not incompatible with medical friendships; and in so doing, let us throw the whole odium of the hostility of physicians to each other upon their competition for business and money. Alas! while merchants, mechanics, lawyers, and the clergy live in a friendly intercourse with each other, and while even the brutes are gregarious, and

"Devil with devil firm concord holds,"

to use the words of Milton, physicians, in all ages and countries, riot upon each others' characters! How shall we resolve this problem in morals?

With love to Mrs. Hosack and Miss Mary, in which all my family join,

I am, dear sir,
Your friend and brother in the republic of medicine,
Benjamin Rush

How a physician should behave toward his patients has always been a matter of great professional concern. Dr. Rush's thoughts on this subject, addressed to a young pupil, have lost nothing of their pertinence over the years.

To William Claypoole, M.D.

July 29, 1782

The following short directions to Dr. Claypoole were given as the parting advice of his old friend and master. If properly attended to, they will ensure him business and happiness in North Carolina.

1. Take care of the poor. By becoming faithful over a few, you will become a ruler over many. When you are called to visit a poor patient, imagine you hear a voice sounding in your ears, "Take care of him, and I will repay thee."

2. Go regularly to some place of worship. A physician cannot be a bigot. Worship with Mohamitans rather than stay at home on Sundays.

3. Never resent an affront offered to you by a *sick* man.

4. Avoid intimacies with your patients if possible, and visit them only in sickness.

5. Never *sue* a patient, but after a year's services get a bond from him if possible.

6. Receive as much pay as possible in goods or the produce of the country. Men have not half the attachment to these things that they have to money.

7. Acquire a habit of visiting your patients *regularly* at one certain hour.

8. Never dispute about a bill. Always make reductions rather than quarrel with an old and profitable patient.

9. Don't insert trifling advice or services in a bill. You can incorporate them with important matters such as a pleurisy or the reduction of a bone.

10. Never make light (to a patient) of *any* case.

11. Never appear in a hurry in a sickroom, nor talk of indifferent matters till you have examined and prescribed for your patient.

To his son James, then a medical student in England, he wrote the characteristic words about the physician's calling:

To his son James

Philadelphia, June 8, 1810

. . . While I thus wish to direct your attention to everything that can improve the gentleman, the philosopher, and the man of the world so as to qualify you to mix with all those classes of people who are to be your patients to advantage, always recollect that your first duties will be to the sick, and that the physician and surgeon should predominate over all other human attainments in your character. . . .

WILLIAM DRENNAN (1754-1820)

A few years after the dreadful yellow fever epidemic in Philadelphia, New York was visited by a severe, though less devastating, outbreak of this terrible disease, whose impact was heightened by the impenetrable mystery surrounding its occurrence. How great its repercussions were becomes evident from the following letter.

The writer, Dr. William Drennan, an Irish physician and poet, is all but forgotten today. His views on international co-operation in medicine and his ideas on disinfection bear the marks of a man well in advance of his time.

To Joseph Wilson, Esq., American Consul

Dublin, October 17, 1799

I feel, as a man ought to feel, for the people of New-York and Philadelphia, suffering under the actual scourge, or the terrifying expectancy, of the Yellow Fever; a malady which may, and perhaps ought to be termed, the Plague of the West, that the selfishness, if not the sympathy of Europe, might be aroused to the means of thoroughly investigating the nature, and counteracting the invisible and creeping progress, of a pestilence, which may, sooner or later, find its way to our own shores. . . .

Alarmed as the United States may be on this subject, I do not think that they are alarmed sufficiently. Too credulous reliance seems to be paid to the suspension of the contagion—the mere torpor of the serpent; and it is surprising that the

Executive of America, whose eyes ought to be as those of a nursing mother over the health of the people, does not offer, or get itself empowered to offer, a large reward, not narrowly restricted to professional men, or the United States, but to the scientific men of *all* nations, some of whom, by the help of an accurate history of this complaint, might hit upon a method of cure, or, what is better, of effectual prevention, which has hitherto escaped the sagacity of practitioners on the spot.

The question agitated so much by, and which so much agitates the Faculty, viz. Whether the fever be imported, or original? seems to me of little comparative importance. There it has been—there it lurks—there it will become endemic. Of what importance, at present, where small-pox or measles had their origin. The great object is an effectual method of cure in the individual patient; and the still greater blessing would be, a perfect means of prevention, the cure universal. . . .

Contagions of different kinds, seem to require a particular temperature which suits their natures, and modifies their force. The small-pox and measles have their particular seasons. The marsh miasmata, vernal and autumnal, are extinguished by the summer heat as well as the cold of winter. With respect to the plague itself, the latest traveller expressly says, that the extremes of *heat* and *cold* both appear to be adverse to it. In Constantinople it is often terminated by the cold of winter, and in Kahira (Cairo) by the heat of summer. . . .

. . . In every apartment, therefore, where an instance of yellow fever *had* occurred, on the removal of the patient by death or recovery, ought not the room to be heated by the use of a portable furnace to a certain high temperature which, without injury to any article, might be sufficient to penetrate to all parts impervious to any vapour, and thus decompose, or at least so much alter the nature of, the adhesive poison as to render it harmless in future?—Might not such an experiment be properly

EDWARD JENNER (1749-1823)

On July 19, 1796, Dr. Edward Jenner, a country doctor in Berkeley, Gloucestershire, sent the following letter to his old friend Edward Gardner:

To Edward Gardner

Berkeley, July 19, 1796

As I promised to let you know how I proceeded in my inquiry into the nature of that singular disease the Cow-Pox, and being fully satisfied how much you feel interested in its success, you will be gratified in hearing that I have at length accomplished what I have been so long waiting for, the passing of the Vaccine Virus from one human being to another by the ordinary mode of inoculation.

A boy of the name of Phipps was inoculated in the arm from a pustule on the hand of a young woman who was infected by her master's cows. Having never seen the disease but in its casual way before; that is, when communicated from the cow to the hand of the milker, I was astonished at the close resemblance of the pustules, in some of their stages, to the variolous pustules. But now listen to the most delightful part of my story. The boy has since been inoculated for the small pox which, as I ventured to predict, produced no effect. I shall now pursue my experiments with redoubled ardour.

Despite all the restraint of this letter, one senses the writer's elation and the awe with which he faces the implications of his discovery. Indeed, he was standing at the threshold of one of the greatest medical advances ever made and at the turning point of his life. Within a few years, hundreds of thousands of people the world over were to be saved from death and disfigurement, and Dr. Jenner was to be transformed from an obscure country practitioner to the most renowned physician of his day. But in the process he was to suffer much heartache.

The story of his discovery has often been told. His overhearing, as a young medical apprentice, of a farm girl's casual remark that she "couldn't take smallpox" because she had had cowpox; the train of thought this remark had started and the strange and enduring fascination it had for him; the long years of experimentation, and the culmination, in the summer of 1796, of his labors by the successful vaccination of a young boy against small pox by inoculation with cowpox "matter," or "vaccine," as we would say today.

How arduous had been the road and how full of obstacles! Not only had he worked under the most primitive conditions, without the benefit of a hospital or laboratory, but also in an age which knew little of the nature of infection and nothing of germs and viruses.

In 1798 Jenner published his famous treatise "An Inquiry into the Causes and Effects of Variolae Vaccinae." He was now nearly fifty years old, and he felt his "evening fast approaching." When, a few months after the publication of the "Inquiry," his medical friends urged him to come to London, predicting "fame and fortune" there, he wrote to one of them:

Cheltenham, September 29, [1798]

. . . My fortune, with what flows in from my profession, is sufficient to gratify my wishes; indeed so limited is my ambition and that of my nearest connexions, that were I precluded from future practice I should be enabled to obtain all I want. And as for fame what is it? a gilded butt, for ever pierced with the arrows of malignancy. . . . In my last letter I told you how much I was perplexed; my perplexity really amounts to agitation. On the one hand, unwilling to come to town myself for the sake of practice, and on the other, fearful that the practice I have recommended may fall into the hands of those who are incapable of conducting it, I am thrown into a state that was at first not perceptible as likely to happen to me; for, believe me, I am not callous to all the feelings of those wounds which, from misrepresentation, might fall on my reputation; on the contrary, no nerves could feel more acutely; and they now are actually in a tremor from anticipation.

How very few are capable of conducting physiological experiments! I am fearful that before we thoroughly understand what is cow-pox matter, and what is not, some confusion may arise; for which I shall, unjustly, be made answerable. . . .

At about this time Dr. George Pearson of London forced himself upon Jenner. On November 8, 1798, Pearson wrote to Jenner saying: "Your name will live in the memory of mankind as long as man possesses gratitude for services, and respect for benefactors; and if I can but get *matter* I am much mistaken if I do not make you live for ever." And five days later we again find him writing: ". . . I wish you could secure for me matter for inoculation. . . ."

Jenner sent him vaccine and Pearson, who became very active in this new field, soon made every attempt to push the little country doctor into the background. A year after his first letter to Jenner his tone had changed appreciably:

George Pearson, M.D. to Edward Jenner

London, Dec. 10, 1799

. . . we have made some progress in the institution of a charity for inoculating the vaccine pock. I do not know that I can confer any honour on you by proposing you (if I am able) to the directors of our establishment, nor do I well know what to propose to you. It occurs to me that it might not be disagreeable to you to be an extra corresponding physician, . . .

No expense is to be attached to your situation except a guinea a-year as a subscriber, and indeed I think you ought to be exempt from that, as you cannot send any patients: but you may depute some proxy in town. . . .

For many more years did this despicable individual try to belittle Jenner's role in the discovery of smallpox vaccination. But fortunately he did not succeed in doing so. Jenner's friends, especially Dr. Lettsom, thwarted his evil designs.

As Jenner had feared and predicted, inoculation with cowpox, or "vaccination" as it was beginning to be called, soon became the object of vehement controversy and he the butt of bitter attacks. However, there also were many who came to his support. In England one of his most ardent admirers was Dr. Lettsom; in America Dr. Benjamin Waterhouse hailed him as one of the greatest benefactors of mankind. Admiration and praise did not turn his head, but the unjust attacks hurt him deeply. To one of his friends he wrote:

To Thomas Paytherus, Esq.

Berkeley, May 12, 1808

. . . Vaccination will go on just as well when I am dead as it does during my existence, probably better, for one obstacle will die with me—Envy.

. . . That such a thing has been discovered, I, in common with the rest of mankind, have reason to rejoice; but this I also declare, that I wish it had been the lot of some other person to have been the discoverer; and in this wish I am sure my family have reason to join me very heartily; for they, as well as myself, are strangers, through it, to those domestic comforts which we should otherwise enjoy. . . .

Dr. Jenner lived to see the success of his method for combating smallpox and he proudly wrote to Lettsom in 1811:

To John C. Lettsom, M.D.

Nov. 22, 1811

. . . I have considered London as the centre of opposition to the Vaccine Practice, but even there, in spite of the base and murderous designs of a few bad-minded individuals, the Small Pox has wonderfully decreased; and in the provinces its mortality has lessened in a still greater proportion. For the great and grand effects of Vaccination the eye must quit this little spot, and survey it among other European countries, and still more particularly among the vast empires of Asia and America. In Mexico and Peru the disease is nearly extinct. The documents which pour in upon me from these distant regions fill me with inexpressible delight. You shall have copies when I can get them transcribed.

The chief impediments to its general adoption here, I am confident, are our newspapers and some of our magazines. Whenever a case of what is called failure starts up, in it goes to a newspaper, with all the exaggeration with which envy and malice can garnish it. . . .

BENJAMIN WATERHOUSE (1754-1846)

Benjamin Waterhouse, the first Professor of Medicine at Harvard Medical School, had the reputation of being one of the best-educated physicians in America. Three years in Europe had brought him in contact with an intellectual atmosphere greatly superior to that then prevailing in the United States. To a man of diversified interests the American scene was not very congenial, and to a physician accustomed to London standards the American practitioner's status might well be distasteful.

In a letter to his friend Dr. Lettsom in London, Waterhouse gives a description of the narrowness of the America of his day which, in the light of other contemporary letters, is undoubtedly not exaggerated.

To John C. Lettsom, M.D.

Cambridge, Nov. 25, 1794

. . . I have no taste for the practice of physic as it is conducted in this country. It is not worth a man's attention. I feel such a mighty difference between transcribing from the great volume of Nature, and practising among the very vulgar, that is, conforming to the whims and nonsense of old women and silly people, that I am sometimes almost determined to renounce it for ever. I know how a London physician gets his bread, but with us it is widely different: a man like me of a weakly frame, addicted to study, is liable to be called out five or six miles on horseback in a severe winter night, and to remain out all night, and to receive (in the course of the year) a guinea for it! We are obliged to be physician, surgeon, apothecary, and tooth-drawer, all under one; and if we are not attentive to small things, and if we do not give consequence to trifles, we are dropped for some one who does. You are spoiled (say some of my friends) for practice in this country, by living so long with Dr. Fothergill, which is in a great measure true—a charming specimen of my intended view of society and manners!

On July 8, 1800, Dr. Waterhouse performed on his young son the first smallpox vaccination in America with Jenner's new method. Other physicians and laymen soon became interested and, as in England, vaccination presently became a hotly debated issue in America. Thomas Jefferson, whose eager mind was ever open to new ideas, was won over to the cause by Waterhouse. A letter from the doctor to Jefferson about the attempts of "not a few" physicians to "corner" smallpox vaccine reflects sadly on their ethical standards.

To President Thomas Jefferson

Cambridge, October 1, 1801

Yesterday I was honored with your letter of Sept. 17th from Monticello informing me that the Vaccine inoculation was effectually planted at Washington, as well as at and near your own residence, and that you had sent the matter to several parts of the State of Virginia. . . . Avarice, rivalship, and mistrust have accompanied its incipient practice in most parts of the Eastern States. . . . I had not a few letters . . . in which the practitioners held out what they conceived luring baites to send them the matter and instructions to the exclusion of their bretheren. Several practitioners rode night and day from the extreme parts of Connecticut and Vermont to Cambridge to get before hand of their neighbours. Sometimes the two rival Doctors of the same town were at my house at the same time, each wishing to outbid the other! An association of six practitioners in New Hampshire absolutely new districted the State, and then applied to me for the matter, and offering me their conjoint bonds to give me a fourth part of all that were inoculated by them and their subordinates! . . . I found myself the centre of a vile speculation. Some went through Vermont and Connecticut calling themselves my agents, commissioned from me to sell the *matter* and spreading a spurious disease and endangering the lives of the people by the abominable cheat. The keenest apostles in this new doctrine went out from Connecticut. I checked, however, this vile traffic in that quarter by exposing the trick in a letter to the President of Yale-College, which he published, with a suitable introduction in his own name. I believe that such speculations would not be so apt to show themselves in the Southern states. I however perceived by letters from that part of the union that some wished to monopolize the practice within certain circles, but the mode I adopted has effectually checked that disposition, and has at the same time given the practice a dignity, which it has never acquired in some parts of the union. . . .

With the highest respect for your character and station, I remain your very humble friend.

Waterhouse was also in frequent correspondence with Jenner. In April, 1802, he sent him the following letter:

To Edward Jenner, M.D.

Cambridge, April 8th, 1802

. . . I believe I informed our friend Dr. Lettsom that the vaccine inoculation was carrying on its salutiferous powers into the wilderness of the new world. If I did not, I will repeat it here.

Last December a grand embassy of certain tribes of the Indians came to the city of Washington while the Congress was sitting, or as they phrase it, while the sixteen *fires* or *lights* were burning. Our Government continued to do every thing to ameliorate their condition. They had sent them seventy ploughs, ten looms, and fifty spinning-wheels, with every common utensil in husbandry, besides establishing blacksmiths, bricklayers, &c. They had taught them to plant orchards, to rear and manage horses, to use scales and weights and measures (for heretofore the white traders used to put in the scales their *foot* or right *hand* against their beaver and ermine skins.) In short, Washington, Adams and Jefferson have done every thing to civilize that shrewd people. The chief of this embassy was named LITTLE TURTLE. The President one day sent for this warrior and his interpreter, and told him that he had a matter of great importance to communicate to him, for the benefit of the whole nation of his RED CHILDREN, for these savages always call him FATHER. He then told him that the GREAT SPIRIT had lately made a precious donation to the enlightened white men over the great water, first to a single person, and from him to another on this side the waters, and then explained to him the history of the cow or kine-pock as a gift from Heaven to preserve them from the small-pox, and even to banish it from the earth. The chief heard him with marked attention, and desired first to receive the benefits of it himself. This was performed soon after by the Rev. Dr. Gautt, chaplain of Congress, and also upon nine or ten more warriors in his train. On their departure the President caused them to be supplied with the virus; and the interpreter (a white man) took a copy of the directions for conducting the process I had transmitted to the President. . . .

Today, Waterhouse is best known as the apostle of vaccination in America. To his contemporaries his "Lecture on Tobacco" apparently had a greater appeal.

To John C. Lettsom, M.D.

Cambridge, May 28, 1807

. . . You mention that on reading over again my Lecture on Tobacco, you was more gratified than at first. I may venture to mention to a friend, that this little production acquired more popularity than any medical or philosophical publication ever printed in America. It excited the attention of all parents who had sons in Colleges. It was popular with every one who had journeymen, apprentices, or clerks, who were apprehensive of fire from smoking cigars. It was popular with the married ladies, whose husbands were in that habit; and it was violently popular with all the young ones who wished for husbands, and hated the smell of tobacco. It was a matter of serious consideration with the clergy, because it called their virtue in question. The subject was a standing joke after dinner, when the fruit, wine, and cigars, were set on the table. Wherever I went in town or country, men, women, and children, were pointing me out as the gentleman who wrote against cigars. Did this feed my vanity? Not absolutely. I was mortified that my labours in Vaccination were, seemingly, less valued than my Smoking Lecture. You perhaps are not aware of the universal prevalence of this nasty custom. Upon nice estimation it was found that *seventy thousand dollars* were consumed in New York, in one year, in cigars. . . .

Despite his many admirable qualities, Waterhouse was eccentric and hard to get along with. His sponsorship of "Doctor" Samuel Thomson and his immoderate letter to Dr. Mitchill show how wrong even a really competent person can on occasion be.

To Samuel L. Mitchill, M.D.

Cambridge, December 19, 1825

. . . I am indeed so disgusted with learned quackery, that I take some interest in honest, humane and strong-minded empiricism; for it has done more for our art, in all ages and in all countries, than all the universities since the time of Charlemagne. Where, for goodness sake, did Hippocrates study?—air, earth and water—man, and his kindred vegetables—diseases and death and all casualties and concomitants of humanity, were the pages he studied—everything that surrounds and nourishes us, were the objects of his attention and study. In a word, he read diligently and sagaciously the Great Book of Nature . . . instead of the books of man.

How came your Legislature to pass so unconstitutional an act as that called the anti-quack law?—such as the Parliament of England would hardly have ventured on?—for who will define quackery? Were I sufficiently acquainted with your excellent Governor Clinton, I would write to him on the subject. You New Yorkers are half a century behind us in theological science, and your quack bill looks as if you halted also in physic. . . .

CHARLES TAFT (ca. 1790-1823)

After completing his apprenticeship with Dr. Spalding, Dr. Taft established himself in a small North Carolina community. Judging from his letter to his "Patron" the young man apparently subscribed wholeheartedly to the old Athenian way of praying: "Let it rain, oh Zeus, on the fields of the Athenians. . . ."

To Lyman Spalding, M.D.

Nixonton, N. C. Jany. 27, 1812

I beg you to excuse me for not writing you ere this, as I render as an excuse, my not having settled myself till now. I am now in the above place, County of Pasquotank, North Carolina, a place as unhealthy as a Physician could wish, if he had any love for his own life. The Fall months are a great harvest to him, if he did not fall a prey, himself. The land is low, very level, and very rich. Therefore, the farmers are wealthy. The people are luxurious in their drinks and diet, their water is intolerably bad, which produces sad work with the intestines. The charges of physicians are very high 40 or 50 cents per mile for travel, emetics 40c, and all other medicine in proportion. I have met with a most cordial reception among the first inhabitants of the places which I have visited; among the common people I succeed, to my mind, by endeavoring to please them with those little assiduities, which hardly ever fail to please ANY ONE. By these means and the advantages I had while under your instruction, and the intense study (which I am determined to pay) I think I shall succeed to the utmost of my wishes in point of employment. . . .

DAVID HOSACK (1769-1835)

David Hosack was a leading figure in medical and social circles in early nineteenth-century New York. For long years one of the young metropolis's most prominent physicians, he counted many of its important citizens among his patients. He also had the singular distinction of being the surgeon in attendance during the Burr-Hamilton duel.

His letter to a young patient is an interesting example of medical thought at the turn of the century. Despite much obviously sound advice it contains recommendations which today appear quite ludicrous and, certainly, the doctor's form of billing is not in keeping with modern concepts of medical decorum.

To a patient

New York April 21 1815

The complaints you describe are of frequent occurrence and are usually with ease removed. They have doubtless been induced in the manner you have stated and are now entirely kept up by the debility induced in the parts affected. The excessive sensibility of the organs concerned is only to be removed by those means which are calculated to improve the strength of the whole system. The filing of iron say grs. 10 taken three times a day in syrup of ginger will be one of the best tonics you can employ. The tinct. of Basle may also occasionally be taken in wine with advantage—bathing the parts affected with cold water night & morning should also be regularly practised—you should

84

also avoid the excitement produced by too much bed-clothing (as heat thus accumulated readily excites the parts affected.) With the same view the accumulation of urine in the bladder should be guarded against by evacuating it at least once in the course of the night. Another mean which I have prescribed with great success for the purpose of preventing the emission of semen is tying a thread around the penis going to bed so that when an erection takes place you are awakened, in that case the emission is prevented. Exercise in the open air—the free use of the most nutritious food especially animal food should also be attended to.—Eggs & milk are especially proper—porter & ale will also be among your best drinks. Sexual intercourse occasionally indulged where circumstances render it proper will also be useful in restoring the natural functions of those parts. At first this capacity may be imperfect—but it will soon return if total abstinence from that habit that induced it be strictly observed—*otherwise* all remedies are useless. But if the patient can abstain from unnatural indulgence he is readily cured by the means I have enumerated.—A ten dollar bill inclosed in your reply will be useful for

yours

D. Hosack.

SIR CHARLES BELL (1774-1842)

Medical care of soldiers in the field was, up to fairly recent times, almost nonexistent. Although barber-surgeons had long accompanied troops, and military surgeons had become part of the armies of the eighteenth century, more effective medical service did not come into being until Florence Nightingale began her humanitarian work in the 1850's.

At the turn of the century, Larrey, Napoleon's great military surgeon, had vastly improved the French Army's care of its wounded. His organization collapsed on the field of Waterloo. Shortly after the battle, Sir Charles Bell, the eminent anatomist and surgeon, went to Brussels to study fresh gunshot wounds. He became more deeply involved than he had anticipated. His description of military surgery in the early nineteenth century, before the introduction of anesthesia, is truly appalling.

To Francis Horner, Esq., M.P.

34, Soho Square, London
July, 1815

I write this to you after being some days at home engaged in my usual occupations, and consequently disengaged of the horrors of the battle of Waterloo. I feel relief in this, for certainly if I had written to you from Brussels, I should have appeared very extravagant. An absolute revolution took place in my economy, body and soul, so that I, who am known to require eight hours sleep, found first three hours, then one hour and a half, sufficient, after days of the most painful excitement and bodily exertion.

After I had been five days engaged in the prosecution of my object, I found that the best cases, that is, the most horrid wounds, left totally without assistance, were to be found in the hospital of the French wounded; this hospital was only forming. They were even then bringing in these poor creatures from the woods. It is impossible to convey to you the picture of human misery continually before my eyes. What was heart-rending in the day was intolerable at night; and I rose and wrote, at four o'clock in the morning, to the chief surgeon, offering to perform the necessary operations upon the French. At six o'clock I took the knife in my hand, and continued incessantly at work till seven in the evening; and so the second and third day.

All the decencies of performing surgical operations were soon neglected. While I amputated one man's thigh, there lay at one time thirteen, all beseeching to be taken next; one full of entreaty, one calling upon me to remember my promise to take him, another execrating. It was a strange thing to feel my clothes stiff with blood, and my arms powerless with the exertion of using the knife! and more extraordinary still, to find my mind calm amidst such variety of suffering; but to give one of these objects access to your feelings was to allow yourself to be unmanned for the performance of a duty. It was less painful to look upon the whole than to contemplate one object.

When I first went round the wards of the wounded prisoners my sensations were very extraordinary. We had everywhere heard of the manner in which these men had fought—nothing could surpass their devotedness. In a long ward, containing fifty, there was no expression of suffering, no one spoke to his neighbour. There was a resentful, sullen rigidness of face, a fierceness in their dark eyes as they lay half covered in the sheets.

Sunday.—I was interrupted, and now I perceive I was falling

into the mistake of attempting to convey to you the feelings which took possession of me, amidst the miseries of Brussels. After being eight days among the wounded I visited the field of battle. The view of the field, the gallant stories, the charges, the individual instances of enterprise and valour recalled me to the sense the world has of victory and Waterloo. But this is transient. A gloomy, uncomfortable view of human nature is the inevitable consequence of looking upon the whole as I did—as I was forced to do.

It is a misfortune to have our sentiments so at variance with the universal impression. But there must ever be associated with the honours of Waterloo, to my eyes, the most shocking sights of woe, to my ear accents of entreaty, outcry from the manly breast, interrupted forcible expressions of the dying, the *noisome smells*. I must show you my notebooks, for as I took my notes of cases generally by sketching the object of our remarks, it may convey an excuse for this excess of *sentiment*.

JOHN COLLINS WARREN (1778-1856)

John Collins Warren did not want to be a physician. An apprenticeship in Boston, to which he had agreed at the earnest desire of his father, had brought medicine no closer to him. But a few weeks in the large hospitals of London changed his views, especially of surgery, so radically that he wrote to his father that he was "surprised" to have been "so long blind."

To his father

London, Dec. 8, 1799

. . . Once, I remember, you asked whether I intended to become a surgeon. The question remains unanswered. At that time, I had seen enough to have an idea of the difficulties of an operation, but none of its pleasures: now I see a good operation with the pleasure I used to feel at the successful solution of Euclid's problems,—a pleasure greater than almost any I know. I have acquired that taste, that high relish, for these, without which no man can exert himself for the attainment of any art; and am only surprised that I was so long blind. . . .

Then, after describing his studies, the letter writer goes on:

. . . Dissection is carried on in style: twelve or fifteen bodies in a room; the young men at work on them in different ways. The people called resurrection-men supply us abundantly. An odd circumstance happened some time since. A hungry beggar had got some bread, and ate with so much avidity as to suffocate himself and fall down in the street. One of the resurrection-men, passing, immediately claimed the man as his brother, took him to the dissecting theatre of St. Thomas, and secured a good price. The man's trachea is now made into a preparation. . . .

The "odd circumstance" alluded to by Warren was, if one takes into consideration the practices of "the people called resurrection-men," probably murder.

Anatomical dissection in England and America was legally still restricted to the bodies of executed criminals; and since the demand for dissecting material was great, recourse was had, as so often under such circumstances, to illegal measures. In order to procure the necessary corpses for their courses, respectable teachers of anatomy did not hesitate to avail themselves of the services of thugs and cutthroats. In the large medical centers of England, bands of criminals raided the cemeteries and burial grounds at night, exhuming freshly interred bodies which they sold at a price to the schools of anatomy. "Body-snatching," as the practice was called, became a highly profitable profession and its practitioners, the "Sack-'em-up-" or "Resurrection-men," were highly paid individuals who, when they saw fit, doubtlessly did not shrink from committing murder.

During his studies in London and Paris, Warren learned how important are hospitals for the instruction of medical students, and how necessary for the medical care of the indigent. On returning to America in 1802, he felt keenly the need of such an institution in Boston. Others, including his father and his friend, Dr. James Jackson, shared his views. Gradually the two young doctors won the support of further members of the community, and in August of 1810 they addressed a circular letter to a number of well-to-do Bostonians in the hope of stimulating their interest in the founding of a "hospital for the reception of lunatics and other sick persons."

Circular letter by James Jackson and John C. Warren

Boston 8/20/1810

It is unnecessary to urge the propriety and even obligation of succouring the poor in sickness. The wealthy inhabitants of the town of Boston have always evinced that they consider themselves as "treasurers of God's bounty;" and in Christian countries, in countries where Christianity is practised, it must always be considered the first of duties to visit and to heal the sick. When in distress, every man becomes our neighbor, not only if he be of the household of faith, but even though his misfortunes have been induced by transgressing the rules both of reason and religion. It is unnecessary to urge the truth and importance of these sentiments to those who are already in the habit of cherishing them—to those who indulge in the true luxury of wealth, the pleasures of charity. The questions which first suggest themselves on this subject are, whether the relief afforded by hospitals is better than can be given in any other way; and whether there are, in fact, so many poor among us as to require an establishment of this sort.

The relief to be afforded to the poor, in a country so rich as ours, should perhaps be measured only by their necessities. We have, then, to inquire into the situation of the poor in sickness, and to learn what are their wants. In this inquiry, we shall be led to answer both the questions above stated.

. . . The amount required for the institution proposed may, at first sight, appear large. But it will cease to appear so, when we consider that it is to afford relief, not only to those who may require assistance during the present year or present age, but that it is to erect a most honourable monument of the munificence of the present times, which will ensure to its founders the blessings of thousands in ages to come; and when we add that this amount may be raised at once, if a few opulent men will contribute only their superfluous income for one year. Compared with the benefits which such an establishment would afford, of what value is the pleasure of accumulating riches in those stores which are already groaning under their weight?

Hospitals and infirmaries are found in all the Christian cities of the Old World; and our large cities in the Middle States have institutions of this sort, which do great honour to the liberality and benevolence of their founders. We flatter ourselves that in this respect, as in all others, Boston may ere long assert her claim to equal praise.

This letter in time led to the founding of the Massachusetts General Hospital, one of the best-known institutions in the United States, and it was here that John Collins Warren performed, in 1846, the first operation on a patient under ether narcosis.

Warren was a deeply religious man who saw a spiritual mission in his medical work.

To a friend

Boston, March 6, 1836

. . . Your suggestions of the expediency of making a change in my professional pursuits have sunk deep into my heart; and I feel more than ever a deep sense of my omissions, and a desire for retirement from the world to repair them. There is a thought which stands in my way. I ask myself, what were the purposes of the Creator in placing me here, giving me experience, and the power of administering relief to my fellow-mortals? Which will be most agreeable in his eyes,—a life of pious thought, or of useful action? Is not the daily recognition of his power and providence, when intermixed with all the acts of life, a more acceptable offering than retirement and contemplation? Cannot I accomplish more by pouring into the ear, which sickness has opened, a seasonable word on righteousness, temperance, and judgment to come, than a reputed religionist could do? . . .

Advice given to his son when the latter was about to go into the practice of medicine shows that Dr. Warren was not only a pious, but also a very practical-minded, Yankee.

To his son

June 7, 1837

. . . Although I wrote yesterday I propose to give you a word more, before I embark, on your peculiar situation. I recollect to have heard it remarked of some one as a great proof of talent that he exactly understood his own position in the world. Few men have this knowledge, though all believe they have it. A correct knowledge of your relations to those around you will be the foundation of your success; a want of this might involve a failure. For a physician of your age you have made a considerable advance in practical standing. To retain and improve this requires greater efforts than ordinary.

An exact and methodical employment of your time. A certain period of it to be devoted to reading, another to writing, and another to daily dissection. I would not allow myself much light reading. It is not only a loss of valuable time, but it weakens our power of reflection. The periods of time not passed in the occupations mentioned should be devoted to patients, or to friends whose society is profitable and useful. Pass as much time with your patients as you can when they are very ill. This is the strongest foundation for affection and confidence. The most successful practitioners have risen on this habit. When you require relaxation go into the society of friends who will promote your interest. Mr. A——, Mr. W——, the G——s, P——s, and others may be rendered immensely valuable; while, if neglected, some other may insinuate himself between you and them. Merit and skill are necessary, but they must be aided by kind attentions, which show that you are interested in their happiness. Above all, our relations may be made our truest friends. Here I wish to caution you against any irritation from apparent want of confidence on the part of patients. This is one of the regular trials of a young practitioner,—one that he must expect to experience even from the lower classes, still more from the higher. Such an expression, however it may operate on the feelings, must not be allowed to influence the external appearance or conduct; for the expression of such irritation is a fair proof that the want of confidence is well founded, since it shows a want of self-command. . . .

RENÉ THÉOPHILE HYACINTHE LAËNNEC
(1781-1826)

One day, in 1816, Dr. Laënnec was consulted by a very stout young woman suffering from a heart condition. Because of her great obesity he found examination of the heart by percussion (thumping) of the chest unsatisfactory. And propriety, he felt, "rendered inadmissible" listening to the action of the heart by placing his ear directly on the chest as he was often in the habit of doing. Caught on the horns of a dilemma he "happened to recollect a simple and well-known fact in acoustics," namely, that sound is augmented when conveyed through certain solid bodies. "Immediately, on this suggestion," he later wrote, "I rolled a quire of paper into a sort of cylinder and applied one end of it to the region of the heart and the other to my ear, and was not a little surprised and pleased, to find that I could hereby perceive the action of the heart in a manner much more clear and distinct than I had ever been able to do by the immediate application of the ear."

During the next two years Laënnec worked intensively on the perfection of his "cylinder," or, as he also called it, "stethoscope." He substituted wood for paper and made numerous other modifications. He examined scores of patients by his new method and checked his observations whenever possible in the autopsy room.

On August 4, 1818 he wrote to a relative.

To his cousin Christophe

Aug. 4, 1818

... My book on the cylinder is just about completed. Not more than forty-eight hours will be needed for it to be ready for publication. The excerpts from it which I have read at the Academy of Medicine and before the faculty have been very well received. It's a real find. Too bad that it wasn't hit upon by certain people who would have known how to make a lot of money out of it. As for me, I'm only a fool in such matters and I will not get more out of it than a little smoke which, to my further detriment, I will not estimate for more than it is really worth.

It is a sad reflection that Laënnec was right in believing that he would not get more than "a little smoke" out of his great discovery. At least not during his lifetime. Pecuniary reward he received almost none and scientific recognition by his colleagues was accorded for the most part only sparingly and often only grudgingly.

Even one of his admirers, the English physician, Sir John Forbes, the translator of his treatise, who had "no doubt whatever" that Laënnec's new method would be "acknowledged to be one of the greatest discoveries in medicine" said of its practicability: "That it will come into general use, notwithstanding its value, I am extremely doubtful; ... It must be confessed that there is something even ludicrous in the picture of a grave physician formally listening through a long tube applied to the patient's thorax. ..."

Such were the opinions of a friend; the criticisms of the detractors were much more severe.

A letter of Laënnec's, written in May, 1826, a few months

before his death from tuberculosis at the age of forty-seven reflects, all its assertions of self-assurance to the contrary, the sentiments of a disappointed man.

To His Excellency, Baron Cuvier, Counsellor of State at
The Royal Gardens

Paris, May 18th, 1826

I have just learned that the awarding of the prize instituted by M. de Montyon for the most useful discovery in the field of medicine is shortly to be made at the Academy of Sciences.

I know that several physicians, members of the commission who had at first overlooked me, are to mention my treatise on auscultation. Within a few days I shall have the honor to send you the second edition of this work.

If the declarations of those of my colleagues who have sought to verify my observations; if those of the Faculties of Medicine in foreign countries in several of which my pupils have already introduced instruction in this new branch of semeiology; if the advantage of being able to include the treatment of hitherto unnoticed lesions in the category of surgical cases; if the numerous favorable results, almost all new, in the field of pathological anatomy, physiology, semeiology, and therapy, of which I shall have the honor to send you a short enumeration; if the discovery, accidental, it must be admitted, of a rich mine of positive facts which I have only been able to discover through a period of ten years of observation and research in hospitals and laboratories, as a result of which my health has broken down for the second time; if finally, the success of this instruction which every year attracts to the Faculty of Medicine and to the Collège de France an extraordinary number of pupils and young physicians from abroad,—should constitute some merit in your opinion, then, perhaps, I need not despair of receiving a favorable decision from the Academy.

I address this communication to you with all the more confidence as I hope that you will have the goodness and patience to obtain confirmation of the accuracy of the facts that I have put before you.

With my respectful consideration, I have the honor to remain, Baron,

your very humble and
very obedient servant,

Twenty years later the great English physician, Thomas Addison wrote: "Were I to affirm that Laënnec contributed more towards the advancement of the medical art than any other single individual, either of ancient or of modern times, I should probably be advancing a proposition which, in the estimation of many, is neither extravagant nor unjust."

JAMES JACKSON (1777-1867)

Dr. James Jackson, the member of a prominent Massachusetts family, was for long years a highly regarded Boston physician and academic teacher. His letters to his son, written during the latter's stay in Paris, contain comments on general aspects of medical thinking which are as valid today as they were more than a century ago. Interesting also is his comment on the difficulties he experienced in learning to use the stethoscope, something a first-year medical student is today expected to master.

To James Jackson, Jr.

Waltham, August 28, 1831

My dear son,

I had the satisfaction yesterday to receive yours of June 26th. Your preceding letter was of June 19th when you were sick, and tho' I presumed that you got well in a day or two, yet I felt uneasy to be two months without any knowledge of you. The fault I know was in the winds. . . .

What you find at the French hospitals is just what I expected —i.e., the means of studying diagnosis and morbid anatomy. You may also gain some knowledge on prognosis. Observe the symptoms and changes in the course of a disease, try to estimate the chances of life or death, of long or short disease, etc., and fix the grounds of your expectation—then compare the result. Observe what others, and particularly the Professor, say on this point and what reasons they give. A physician need not always declare

99

his prognosis, but he should always try to make one for himself—
it decides the treatment—the greater the danger, the bolder may
be the treatment, if any reliance is to be placed on treatment.

As to therapeutics—we often do too much—the French too
little. You may perhaps get so well acquainted with Andral or
some other such man as to suggest, at some future day, that you
have been accustomed to see such and such treatment and ask
whether this has been tried in Paris and rejected, etc. Such suggestions modestly made may lead to useful discussions—possibly
they may be willing to try the American mode, tho' not the
English. . . .

I have applied for your degree of A.M., and will send you the
diploma. . . . I hope that you will not neglect your exercise any
more—you see that you lose time by it. I thought you were sufficiently impressed on that subject. To gain knowledge even is useless at the expense of health. Health is physical virtue and is
second only in importance to moral virtue. . . .

Boston, January 6, 1832

My dear son,

On the 1st I received yours of the 28th Oct. It is on the use
of the stethoscope, its difficulties. I believe that I wrote you in
the same month stating the difficulties on my part. I scarcely
expect to overcome them—yet I expect you to do it. It is in-
comparably easier for you than for me, and you will have great
opportunities abroad. . . .

Boston, February 14, 1832

My dear son,

. . . Do not cease to write me on the topics which engage your
mind. I only wish I could answer you while the interest lasts. I
know the difficulties attending diseases of the brain both acute

and chronic—and I am glad the subject has engaged your attention while you have opportunities of studying it practically. You
duly appreciate the difficulty of recognizing diseases in their forming state. It has been the study of my life to overcome this difficulty. In respect to acute diseases the opportunity for getting
this information is greatest in private practice and with patients
of the first class who send early and give all the details. In
chronic diseases the cases rarely come before us at the first,—
or, at least, they often do not, even in private practice. It is, however, a great help to have acquired first a knowledge of diseases
when fully developed, and of their morbid anatomy. It is this
which you now have the opportunity of doing. I hope in two
years from this time to put your ears in use at my hospital. I
think you will find that I have made some progress in the use of
my own—tho' less than you have. My opportunities have been
very great for two months past—and I have not neglected them
entirely, but have not had time to use them fully. I have been
truly pressed by business—scarcely getting time for my newspaper some days. Today I gave my last lecture for this season—
and to-morrow begin examinations.

I am willing to hear that you take some interest in political
subjects. But do not allow yourself to do anything or to pledge
yourself on such subjects. The world is going through a great
change. I do not doubt that its results will be salutary—but
zealots will retard the good by their eagerness to hasten it—and
the wily will avail themselves of the zeal of honest men to do
much harm for selfish purposes.

Much has been written in recent years on the influence of the
psyche on bodily functions. The views expressed in the following
letter may possibly be called "psychosomatic medicine in re-
verse."

To Miss Anna C. Lowell

Boston, November 12, 1843

. . . Dyspepsy and cheerfulness do not go together. . . . Again too I am aware that you poetical people are able to describe misery so well as to make us prosaic folks realize it to the utmost, and often more than you mean to. . . . I believe that philosophy is a feeble antagonist to dyspepsy. The latter can raise clouds faster than the former can dispel them or blow them away. When the stomach rights itself and the complexion assumes a fresher hue, philosophy sometimes struts in and boasts of the smiles it has brought and the resignation it has inspired. It is hard to fight with the demon in his moment of power. I believe the best one can do is to fix in the mind a conviction that the black and motley crew of despondent thoughts are of fleshly origin, and not, as they would pretend, from a spiritual source. And second to engage the mind as much as possible in some occupation, or rather on some occupation. Now it is just so you do, I believe, and as usual I finish without recommending anything new. . . .

JAMES JACKSON, JR. (1810-1834)

The "dear son" to whom some of the preceding letters were addressed, James Jackson, Jr., had like so many physicians' sons chosen medicine for his profession. After studying under his father and attending lectures at Harvard Medical School he went to Paris to complete his medical education. Paris was then the world's foremost medical center and many young American physicians there availed themselves of the opportunity of perfecting their knowledge before entering the practice of medicine.

Young Jackson was generally recognized as being a physician of exceptional promise. Louis, the famous clinician, one of his teachers in Paris, predicted for him a brilliant career. Indeed, his outlook was most propitious. The son of a highly esteemed physician, socially well connected and personally well liked, everything pointed to a useful and successful life. A few months after his return to Boston he became seriously ill. After an apparent recovery he died unexpectedly, shortly after his 24th birthday.

His father erected a monument to his memory in a most touching document, the "Memoir of James Jackson, Jr., M.D." Again and again the elder Jackson stresses his objectivity in the evaluation of his son. But, "who will believe that I shall be impartial? . . . I might seem an improper person to give his history, and my statements may be deemed scarcely worthy of credit."

The departed had been every hour in his mind. "In every occupation, in almost every conversation, however little others could see the connection, his image has been before me. It has been a beautiful image. . . . He loved me as few sons loved their father."

In Paris young Jackson became acquainted with Laënnec's

method of auscultation about which he writes to his father in his very first letter from there.

To his father

Paris, October 28, 1831

I feel almost disposed to cover a sheet or two in enumerating the difficulties of auscultation. If Laënnec has added an important aid to our insufficient means of exploring diseases of the chest, he has, at the same time, rendered the study of those diseases more difficult, more laborious I would say, to the learner. Perhaps we may better say, in other words, that this great observer has so far extended our knowledge upon this subject, by his accurate distinctions, that the labor, requisite to obtain all that is known, is much greater than it has hitherto been. I have just returned from the Hôpital des Enfans, where I have been experiencing the difficulties and the uncertainties of auscultation. I have been employed for nearly an hour in examining two children, in both of whom there is some reason to suspect the existence of tubercles. . . .

The knowledge to be gained by the auscultation of infants is much greater than I had supposed. There are certain points of great difficulty, like that I have mentioned; but as to others, on the contrary, there is a great facility. . . . For my part, I can never henceforth examine a child under disease without bringing to my aid this means. . . .

In the spring of 1832 there was an outbreak of cholera in Paris, one of the dreaded epidemic diseases of the time. It had originated in the East and was spreading westward through Europe. Would it reach America? Little could be done to stem its progress or to treat its victims. Clearly, it was his duty, Jackson felt, to stay and learn what could be learned.

To his father

Paris, April 1, 1832

I lament to tell you that the cholera, which was yet a little doubtful when I last wrote, (three days since,) is now reigning in Paris; and I must add to a frightful degree. You will learn details from the journals. To this moment there are at least three hundred cases, and a full half already dead. But you are anxious for me;—you suffer because I still remain here;—perhaps you even reproach me with an undue inattention to the rights and feelings of my family. A word upon this subject. 1st. What is my actual danger? I do not deny that the first blow is very strong, in truth frightfully so. But who are the subjects affected? Up to this moment, *exclusively* the lower classes. I have inquired of many physicians and among them of those whose practice is extensive; —they have not seen a man in easy circumstances affected;—the journals say the same. Thus as yet my danger is very slight, though living in the midst of disease. But again, why need I stay in Paris? In the first place, the disease came upon us so suddenly that we had no time to leave. On Wednesday I first heard of its existence, and already, Sunday, there are three hundred patients. We could not have left the first day, for we were not yet assured; and now what are my circumstances? I am here with perhaps thirty American students, and of them all, I may say with truth, my mind has not been the least occupied with medicine for some years. We are in a city where we may see a disease of the most frightful nature,—which will, in all probability, soon reach our own dear country. We are bound as men and physicians to stay and see this disease;—as a physician you know it and feel it;—

as a father you dread it. For myself, I confess, I should be unwilling to return to America, and not have at least made an effort to learn the nature and the best treatment of this destroyer of life. I feel bound to remain with the rest;—for no one thinks, as yet, of leaving. . . .

Now, for the disease;—one word;—it is death. Truly, at Hôtel Dieu, where I have seen fifty and more in a ward, it is almost like walking through an autopsy room;—in many nothing but the act of respiration shows that life still exists. It is truly awful.—As for treatment, nothing is yet decided. I cannot find that any of the thousand different modes essayed is in truth very powerful;— and certainly, whatever be their potency, their effect is almost null. The physicians are in a state of the greatest incertitude, not knowing which way to turn. I cannot pretend to give you any detailed account of symptoms or treatment.

I can only say that the disease is in truth almost a conversion instantaneously from life to death.

In young Jackson's day medicine was just beginning to emerge from the depths it had been in for centuries. It was about to become a science. Men like himself clearly recognized its shortcomings and foresaw in what direction it would have to progress.

To a friend

Paris, June 18, 1833

. . . Do you mean to overwhelm me with ridicule? When I have chosen my science, and you yours, do you think it just to take it for granted that, because the one is eminently calculated to develope the mind's best powers and the soul's best affections, the other cannot and is not equally so? As a scientific man, you must surely forget yourself, when you attempt to prove that botany, or geology, or any other of the sciences, *as a science*, is better calculated to improve the intellect, or to afford pleasure to the student, than is medicine; or, rather, the accessory sciences which compose it. What is the pleasure, what the occupation of a truly scientific man? Surely, from an exact and detailed observation of what his senses can demonstrate to him, upon a given subject, to trace the great general laws of nature upon that subject. This I maintain to be the fundamental attraction of every science, to one who will view the subject as a man of science should. This being taken for granted, and I think you will hardly deny it me, I would beg you to point out the real distinction, *scientifically speaking*, between tracing the pollen-tubes to the ovula of an asclepias, with the eye, and following with the ear the various modifications of sound produced in the chest by a pneumonia. Why, with my stethoscope, may I not as much enjoy a crepitous râle, (of the first order,) or a bronchial respiration of the purest tone, as Brown, with his microscope, a little channel leading from one part to another of his flower. In both cases what do we do? Appreciate, by the nice use of our senses, the phenomena appreciable by them, and then from those phenomena, connected with our previous knowledge, arrive at some law of the existence of these two *beings*; an asclepias on the one hand, a pneumonia upon the other. Perhaps I deceive myself; but I think not; if any distinction exists between these two things, point it out, I pray of you. The reason that medicine, (or, to use a better term, the reason that pathology and therapeutics, or the natural history of disease before and after death, and the influence of external agents upon the march of disease,) is so despised as a science, is, that it has never yet been studied as a *science*. But the time has come; it actually now takes the rank with the other sciences; only it is the least advanced of them. We have learned that *positive* knowledge may be gained, where we formerly admitted

THOMAS LOVELL BEDDOES (1803-1849)

Thomas Lovell Beddoes was born into a well-to-do upper middle class English family on July 20, 1803. While at school he began writing poetry and as a nineteen-year-old student at Oxford he published a drama, *The Bride's Tragedy*, which found considerable acclaim. During the next few years he led the life of a promising young man of letters in London. And then, apparently on the threshold of a distinguished literary career, he suddenly made a break with the past. He abandoned his literary pursuits and, leaving England, he went to Germany to study medicine. His friends at home deplored his decision and attempted to persuade him to return to literature. In reply to a letter from Thomas Kelsall, his closest associate, he wrote from Göttingen giving his reasons for his decision.

To Thomas Forbes Kelsall

Göttingen Dec. 4, 1825
Sunday

. . . I think you will not fear that I shall become at any time a bare & barren man of science, such as are so abundant & so appallingly ignorant on this side of Chemistry or Anatomy. Again, even as a dramatist, I cannot help thinking that the study of anatomy phisol-psych: & anthropology applied to and illustrated by history, biography and works of imagination is that which is most likely to assist one in producing correct and masterly delineations of the passions: great light would be thrown on Shakespeare by the commentaries of a person so educated. The studies then of the dramatist & physician are closely, almost inseparably, allied; the application alone is different; but is it impossible for the same man to combine these two professions in some degree at least?

The science of psychology, & mental varieties has long been used by physicians, in conjunction with the corresponding corporeal knowledge, for the investigation & removal of immaterial causes of disease; it still remains for some one to exhibit the sum of his experience in mental pathology & therapeutics, not in a cold technical dead description, but a living semiotical display a series of anthropological experiments developed for the purpose of ascertaining some important psychical principle—i.e. a tragedy.

. . . You talk about too much practice & so forth. I believe that is what is least to be feared; I am very nearly unconnected, am not apt at flattery or the social humiliations to which the fashionable physician is bound. . . .

WAITSTILL R. RANNEY (1792-1854)

Few physicians have had a higher regard for their calling nor have many derived greater intellectual and moral satisfaction from the study and practice of medicine than Waitstill Ranney. Born and bred in southern Vermont toward the end of the eighteenth century, he spent almost his entire life in the narrow confines of this rural community.

A poor farm boy who made possible his professional education through utmost perseverance and application, he established himself as a physician at the age of twenty-two in the hamlet of West Townshend, Vermont. If the life of a country practitioner is rarely an easy one, it was especially difficult for young Dr. Ranney. Competition was strong and remuneration of professional services so miserable that he found it necessary to supplement the income from his practice by farming; and he had to combine the two so exacting professions of physician and farmer until he was forty-five years old.

His eldest son, despite the trials and tribulations of his father, in time also became a physician. The following letters are addressed to him by his father when he was a young student and a freshman doctor. They clearly show what kind of man this simple country doctor was and how discerning and critical a physician he must have been.

To his son

. . . The profession in which we are engaged is one of immense responsibility. By a mistake in the vials; by a hurried proscription;

by a want of proper discrimination, or of adequate qualification, an individual may be ushered into eternity; his earthly career of happiness or usefulness may be permanently terminated, and possibly a soul thrust into the presence of its Maker in an unprepared state. I have often thought if the people knew how poorly their doctors are qualified for the places they attempt to fill, they would fear sickness much more than they do. Sure, some are, to an extent, aware of this, and do not repose that confidence in their medical advisers that they really deserve. But there are others, and very many, too, who suppose doctors know all about their case in every particular; can weigh and estimate all the dangers, and even predict the moment of their recovery or death. Now it is difficult to say which are most to be pitied. I rather prefer doctering the first class than the last. Both are deceived, and yet, the first having no confidence to lose, I am safe in an *emergency*: if *unsuccessful* I lose nothing—if successful, some confidence may be acquired. Another idea—the science of medicine is quite imperfect, notwithstanding all the boasted improvements that have been made.

How little that is unquestionably *certain* is in possession of the wisest! As an illustration, look at the theories of fever, and see what contradictions of theory, and how inconsistencies of practice are inculcated by authorities of equal celebrity. Such is the ignorance on these points that it is a question whether any practice at all interrupts, or cures, a fever. What *names* have been and are attached or abolished anon?

Dr. Chandler once, on being asked what *kind* of a fever his patient had, replied in his usual rough manner, "A d——d hot fever." The most popular theory of the cause of fever at the present day is, "poison in the blood," and "fever curers" are the butt of ridicule by learned professors and medical philosophers.

Dr. Twitchell, it is said, made his fever patients the regular morning and evening visits, told his stories, laughed and chatted with the family, but invariably went away without ordering any medicine. The father of one of his patients followed him to his carriage one day and enquired what he meant by such a course? "Mean," says the Dr., "I mean to have your son live!"

This implies what many observing doctors will not deny, that the chances of recovery are not always increased by medication, but *may* be diminished. Many old physicians in my acquaintance have become quite sceptical in advanced life in regard to using drugs at all in many diseases. Hence has arisen Homeopathy, Hydropathy, &c., &c.

But what are we to infer from all this? That the regular practice of medicine is a humbug, to be abandoned by all honest men?

By no means. Study it still more attentively; compare your book knowledge with actual observation at the bed-side. Be governed less by fanciful theories than incontrovertible facts— ("stubborn things.") It is better to let your patients die with the "powerful operation" of *bread pills* and colored drops from the "north side of the well," than to suffer medication misapplied. . . .

Oct. 9, 1831

. . . The practice of the profession, for the most part, has been to me delightsome. To be the instrument in alleviating distress and prolonging life, is highly gratifying to every feeling heart. To reflect upon the wonderful structure and functions of the living body, both in health and disease, as well as upon the operation of medicinal agents, affords a satisfaction indescribable, and tends to give us an exalted opinion of the Deity Himself. I have only to regret that my opportunities were so limited, and that my time since I commenced practice has been so much occupied with labors and cares connected with my family and farm as to afford too little leisure for professional reading.

It is true that there are severe trials connected with the practice of medicine. We must witness the dying struggles of our patients, and painfully learn the insufficiency of the healing art. We must hear their cries for relief, and be incapable of affording it. We must attend to midnight calls, brave the storm and tempest, and sometimes with very slight prospects of compensation. But, humanity suffers, and we must go. And it is sometimes true, and not to be denied, that often ingratitude and abuse is all the remuneration obtained for privations and services performed with the best of motives; though generally we secure the affections of the virtuous and discerning, and are generously rewarded for the labor bestowed.

On the whole, perhaps there is no profession that affords a fairer prospect of ample support than the medical, when prosecuted with unremitting zeal and faithfulness. . . .

JOHANN STIEGLITZ (1767-1840)

One of the most difficult questions a physician can be confronted with is what to tell a patient suffering from an incurable disease. An almost equally grave decision concerns his choice of therapy in such a situation. Should he confine himself to alleviating the patient's suffering without prolonging life unnecessarily, or is he obligated to institute measures which, according to current knowledge, cannot effect a cure but will keep the patient alive longer, perhaps at the expense of his subjective well-being?

Dr. Johann Stieglitz, a highly respected German physician, writing to a young medical friend in the early part of the last century, had the following to say about these problems:

To K. F. H. Marx, M.D.

December 15, 1826

. . . One can frequently hear people say that they do not fear death but are afraid of dying. . . .

. . . I have often thought it would be important to instruct physicians how to behave in cases of incurable disease; not so much to tell them what to do, but rather what not to do.

I am often outraged when, in cases of large tumors, of carcinoma, of unquestionable protracted glaucoma and in innumerable other instances, I see elaborate therapeutic plans being developed when no one can doubt that the disease is incurable. A newly consulted physician starts doing all over what the others had already long done. . . . The patient often wishes to be told clearly whether he must expect to die and whether death now be inevitable.

Reasons are offered to show how important it would be to have this information and to prove with what fortitude and resignation he would be able to accept it. The physician may never take away all hope. An artillery-officer shot himself in Berlin on the staircase of Selle's house after having insisted that the latter tell him the truth about his tuberculosis, and he then didn't even wait till he got home. During the early years of this century I too had an experience, under entirely different circumstances, which has caused me never to tell the whole truth in such cases. Man doesn't want others to unequivocally express even what is perfectly clear to him if it is of evil nature and affects him. He still wants to be able occasionally to believe that the contrary may be possible. . . .

The correspondence between the two doctors deals also with many other aspects of a medical man's philosophy. Dr. Stieglitz's views on the limitations of medicine and on its spiritual qualities are well worth preserving:

To K. F. H. Marx, M.D.

April 10, 1830

In answer to your only too correct complaint about the deficiencies and limitations of our knowledge and achievements I can only say: our science and art are indeed only fragmentary and will essentially remain so, notwithstanding all the worthwhile piecemeal progress that will be made in the course of time. Nevertheless, . . . one must admire how far our knowledge has progressed, especially in recent times. Insight into life itself, its origins, its nature is forever denied to man on earth. It is the destiny of mankind that at all times many individuals must suffer and die from disease. A greater perfection of medicine would not be in harmony with this course of events. It is, in part, the calling of the physician to so render assistance that, through the trust placed in him and by his personal and professional influence, the most trying situations, the greatest dangers and death itself will be borne with greater fortitude and resignation. . . .

SAMUEL HAHNEMANN (1755-1843)

Samuel Hahnemann, the inventor of homeopathy, was a man of many parts. Well-educated and intelligent, he nevertheless conceived a medical "system" as grotesque as any of the preposterous systems of his day. Revolted by the crudeness of medical practice, he turned his back on medicine and, taking up chemistry, he was on his way to becoming a very good chemist when he turned again to medicine to become the founder of Homeopathy. "He would have made a great chemist," said the famous chemist Berzelius, "had he not become a great quack."

Despite all the muddle-headedness of his system, Hahnemann had real medical insight as is obvious from the advice contained in the following letter to a patient, an apparently very busy tailor.

To a patient

. . . For the present I must say that you are on the fair road to health, and the chief sources of your malady cut off. One source still remains, and it is the cause of your last relapse. Man (the delicate human machine) is not constituted for overwork, and he cannot overwork his powers or faculties with impunity. If he does so from ambition, love of gain, or other praiseworthy or blameworthy motive, he sets himself in opposition to the order of nature, and his body suffers injury or destruction. All the more if his body is already in a weakened condition; what you cannot accomplish in a week you can do in two weeks. If your customers will not wait they cannot fairly expect that you will for their sakes make yourself ill and work yourself to the grave, leaving your wife a widow and your children orphans. It is not only the greater bodily exertion that injures you, it is even more the attendant strain on the mind, and the overwrought mind in its turn affects the body injuriously. If you do not assume an attitude of cool indifference, adopting the principle of living first for yourself and only secondly for others, then there is small chance of your recovery. When you are in your grave men will still be clothed, perhaps not as tastefully, but still tolerably well. . . .

. . . The everlasting pushing and striving of blinded mortals in order to gain so and so much, to secure some honor or other, to do a service to this or that great personage—this is generally fatal to our welfare, this is a common cause of young people ageing and dying before their time. . . .

. . . In order to win the race, quickness is not all that is required. Strive to obtain a little indifference, coolness and calmness . . . Then shall your blood course through your blood vessels calmly and sedately, without heat. No horrible dreams disturb the sleep of him who lies down to rest without highly strung nerves . . . Let restless, selfdestroying men act as irrationally, as injuriously towards themselves as they please; let them be fools. But be you wiser! . . . .

Hahnemann also had strong convictions concerning the dignity of the medical man. Although the tone of his letter to a young disciple may repulse us by its Teutonic overbearingness, it must in many ways command our respect.

To a young physician

Coethen, June 19, 1826

. . . make your visits to your patients rarer; keep up your dignity, and more frequently withdraw your attendance on patients who do not show sufficient confidence in you, if they do not show more respect for you and your art.

You should never allow yourself to be dismissed, but when ever a patient does not do exactly as you desire, or ceases to talk in becoming terms, you should at once take leave of him; "You don't act as I wish, but do so and so against my orders; employ whom you will, I will have nothing more to do with you;" and this do to one after another. . . . This would at first deprive you of a few patients who are of no importance, but in course of time, if you persist in your authoritative manner, you will be respected and sought after, and none will dare to use any liberties with you. It is better to be without patients, and devote yourself to study, keeping up your dignity, than to stand in such a relation with patients. . . . If any of your patients is not entirely submissive dismiss him summarily, even though by such conduct you should only retain two, or one single patient, or should be left without any. They would return by degrees, with more respect, submissiveness and humility, and more disposed to pay well. . . . Rather suffer penury, which you are not likely to do, than abate one jot of your own dignity, or that of the art you practice. . . .

JOHN CONOLLY (1796-1866)

The lot of the patients in the insane asylums of the eighteenth century was dreadful beyond description. Exposed to the sadistic brutality of wardens recruited from the dregs of society and to the medical care of physicians who, lacking all understanding of the nature of their disease, subjected them—by way of therapy—to incredible physical and mental torture, these unfortunates pined away their days manacled, beaten and starved, in punishment for deeds over which they had no control.

Toward the end of the century there was a gradual turn for the better. The worst abuses were mitigated little by little. And in 1796, Dr. Phillipe Pinel, with the express permission of the French National Assembly, freed his mental patients at the Salpêtrière Hospital in Paris from their handcuffs, chains and straitjackets. Despite this great example, progress was only slow. Pinel's ideas were accepted but haltingly and with many reservations, and for several decades almost all European and American asylums adhered to the old methods.

In 1839, Dr. John Conolly, an ardent admirer of Pinel, was put in charge of the large mental institution at Hanwell, England. He immediately abolished restraints. He treated the inmates like sick people and not like dangerous animals. It was a daring and courageous thing to do, about which he wrote to a friend a few months later:

October 1839

I know you will be glad to hear that we have now ruled this great house for four months without a single instance of restraint by any of the old and objectionable methods. The use of strait-waistcoats is abolished; hand-straps and leg-locks are never re-sorted to; and the restraint chairs have been cut up to make a floor for the carpenter's shop. All this has, of course, occasioned some trouble and some anxiety; but the success of the plan, and its visible good effects, abundantly repay me. I think I feel more deeply interested in my work every day. I meet with the most constant and kind support of the magistrates; indeed, my only fear is that they should say too much of what is done here, and thus provoke enmity and censure.

Our asylum is now almost daily visited by the officers of other institutions, who are curious to know what method of restraint we *do* resort to; and they can scarcely believe that we rely wholly on constant superintendence, constant kindness, and firmness when required.

JOHN WARE (1795-1864)

When Dr. John Ware returned to Boston in the late fall of 1846 he found physicians everywhere talking of a medical innovation which was apparently destined to revolutionize surgical practice. On October 16th old Dr. John Collins Warren, Boston's most prominent surgeon, had operated, before a highly skeptical audience, on a patient rendered unconscious and insensible to pain through the inhalation of ether. Since then other men had used ether with equally gratifying results. At last, it seemed, a way had been found to overcome the horrors attending upon surgical operations.

In a letter to the *British and Foreign Medical Review* Dr. Ware describes the new procedure:

To the Editor of the *British and Foreign Medical Review*

Boston, November 29, 1846

I found, on my arrival here, a new thing in the medical world, or rather the new application of an old thing, of which I think you will like to hear. It is a mode of rendering patients insensible to the pain of surgical operations, by the inhalation of the vapour of the strongest sulphuric ether. They are thrown into a state nearly resembling that of complete intoxication from ardent spirits or of narcotism from opium. This state continues but a few minutes—five to ten—but, during it, the patient is insensible to pain. A thigh has been amputated, a breast extirpated, teeth drawn, without the slightest suffering. The number of operations of various kinds, especially those in dentistry, has been very considerable, and I believe but few persons resist the influence of the agent.

The effect is not exactly the same on all. In some, the insensibility is entire, and the patient is aware of nothing which is going on; in others, a certain degree of the power of perception remains, the patient knows what the operator is doing, perceives him, for example, take hold of a tooth and draw it out, feels the grating of the instrument, but still has no pain.

There are no subsequent ill effects to detract from the value of this practice, none even so great as those which follow a common dose of opium. One person told me she had some unpleasant sensations in the head for a short time, and was weak, languid, and faintish through the day, but not more so than she ordinarily was from having a tooth drawn. Another told me that he experienced something of the same kind and in addition that his breath smelt very strongly of *ether* for forty-eight hours, and was indeed so strongly impregnated with it as to affect the air of the room in which he sat, so as to be disagreeable to others.

One of our best operative surgeons informs me that he regards it as chiefly applicable to cases of the large and painful operations which are performed rapidly, and do not require any very nice dissection, but that for the more delicate operations, which require some time, he would prefer to have the patient in his usual state. But it is impossible at present to judge what will be the limits to the application of such an agent. Objections may arise of which we do not dream, and evils may be found to follow, which we do not now perceive. Still it certainly promises much in surgery, and perhaps may be capable of application for other purposes beside the alleviation of pain. Would it not be worthy of trial in tetanus, in asthma, and in various cases of violent internal pain especially from supposed spasms?

It was brought into use by a dentist, and is now chiefly employed by that class of practitioners. He has taken out a patent for the discovery, and has despatched persons to Europe to secure one there also; so you will soon hear of it and probably have an opportunity of witnessing its effects.

SIR JAMES Y. SIMPSON (1811-1870)

James Simpson was born on June 7, 1811 in Bathgate, Scotland, the son of a baker of very modest means. Early recognizing in him its most brilliant member, his family made it possible, especially through the help of two older sons, to send him to study medicine at Edinburgh.

His intelligence, industry and untiring perseverance soon secured him professional recognition and, at the age of twenty-nine, he was made Professor of Obstetrics at the University. A highly esteemed teacher and scientist, he was also a much sought-after medical practitioner.

When, in January, 1847, one of his devoted patients, the Duchess of Sutherland, notified him that Queen Victoria was about to appoint him one of "Her Majesty's Physicians for Scotland," he wrote to his brother Alexander:

To Alexander Simpson

January 1847

I believe you will be glad to hear that I am to be appointed one of Her Majesty's Physicians for Scotland. The death of Dr. Davidson (who succeeded Dr. Abercrombie) has left a vacancy in the Scotch Royal Household. Her Grace the Duchess of Sutherland wrote directly to the Queen wishing for my appointment, and she has sent me an extract from a letter of Her Majesty to her Grace, saying that she (the Queen) would nominate me, 'which' (to quote the Queen's note) 'his high character and abilities make him very fit for.' Flattery *from the Queen* is perhaps *not* common flattery, but I am far less interested in it than in having delivered a woman this week *without* any pain while inhaling sulphuric ether. I can think of naught else. . . .

Ever since he had seen, as a young student, the terrible agony of a poor Highland woman while undergoing an operation for removal of the breast, an experience so harrowing to him that he almost decided against becoming a physician, he had been asking: "Can anything be done to make operations less painful?" At last his fond wish was apparently to go into fulfillment.

Thrilled by the news from Boston that a successful operation had been performed on a patient who had been made totally unconscious and insensible through inhalation of ether, he had hastened to use this drug in the delivery room.

Not fully satisfied with ether he started a search for a more powerful anesthetic. He found it in chloroform which, much more potent but also more poisonous than ether, was destined for half a century to replace it almost entirely. The introduction of chloroform anesthesia made Simpson one of the most famous and revered physicians of his time.

In a letter to a physician in Liverpool he has described some of his early experiences with this narcotic.

To a physician

Edinburgh, 14 Nov. 1847

I send you the first of the enclosed papers which I have myself sent off. My wife sent two yesterday—one, I think, to

Dr. Petrie. I am sure you will be delighted to see part of the good results of our hasty conversation. I think I will get hold yet of some greater things in the same way.

I had the chloroform for several days in the house before trying it, as, after seeing it such a heavy unvolatile-like liquid, I despaired of it, and went on dreaming about others.

The first night we took it Dr. Duncan, Dr. Keith, and I all tried it simultaneously, and were all 'under the table' in a minute or two.

I write in great haste, as I wish to scribble off several letters.

Be so good as say what you think may be the ultimate selling price of an ounce of it? Duncan and Flockhart charge 3s. for the ounce.

There has been a great demand for the pamphlet yesterday at the booksellers' here.—Yours very truly,

P.S.—By the bye, Imlach tells me Dr. P. is to enlighten your medical society about the 'morality' of the practice. I have a great itching to run up and pound him. *When* is the meeting?

The true moral question is, 'Is a practitioner justified by *any* principles of humanity in not using it?' I believe every operation without it is just a piece of the most deliberate and cold-blooded *cruelty*.

He will be at the primary curse, no doubt. But the word translated 'sorrow' is truly 'labour,' 'toil;' and in the very next verse the very same word means this.

Adam was to eat of the ground with 'sorrow'. That does not mean *physical* pain, and it was cursed to bear 'thorns and thistles,' which we pull up without dreaming that it is a sin.

God promises repeatedly to take off the two curses on women and on the ground, if the Israelites kept their covenant. See Deut. vii. 13, etc. etc. See also Isaiah xxviii, 23; extirpation of the 'thorns and thistles' of the first curse said to come from God.

Besides, Christ in dying 'surely hath borne our griefs and carried our sorrows,' and removed 'the curse of the law, being made a curse for us.' His mission was to introduce mercy, not sacrifice.

Go up and refute him if I don't come.

Incredible as it may seem "Dr. P." was not to remain the only person to voice objections to the use of anesthetics. In criticism of this attitude a physician, Dr. George Wilson, wrote a remarkable letter to Simpson describing the mental and physical anguish of an operation performed on him before, as Charles Darwin has called them, "the blessed days of chloroform."

George Wilson, M.D., to Sir James Y. Simpson

I have recently read, with mingled sadness and surprise, the declarations of some surgeons that anaesthetics are needless luxuries, and that unendurable agony is the best of tonics. Those surgeons, I think, can scarcely have been patients of their brother surgeons, and jest at scars only because they never felt a wound; but if they remain enemies of anaesthetics after what you have written, I despair of convincing them of their utility. My present object in writing is not to supplement your arguments in favour of the administration of anaesthetics to those who are about to undergo surgical operations; but, as one who knows from personal experience what operations were to the patients before ether or chloroform was employed anaesthetically, I am anxious to state certain reasons in justification of their use, which only those who suffered without their help are in a condition to urge.

Several years ago, I was required to prepare, on very short warning, for the loss of a limb by amputation. A painful disease, which for a time had seemed likely to yield to the remedies employed, suddenly became greatly aggravated, and I was informed by two surgeons of the highest skill, who were consulted on my case, that I must choose between death and the sacrifice of a limb, and that my choice must be promptly made, for my strength was fast sinking under pain, sleeplessness, and exhaustion.

The week, so slow, and yet so swift in its passage, at length came to an end, and the morning of the operation arrived. There were no anaesthetics in those days, and I took no preparative stimulant or anodyne of any kind, unless two cups of tea, which with a fragment of toast formed my breakfast, be considered such.

The operation was a more tedious one than some which involve much greater mutilation. It necessitated cruel cutting through inflamed and morbidly sensitive parts, and could not be despatched by a few swift strokes of the knife. I do not suppose that it was more painful than the majority of severe surgical operations are, but I am not, I believe, mistaken in thinking that it was not less painful, and this is all that I wish to contend for.

Of the agony it occasioned, I will say nothing. Suffering so great as I underwent cannot be expressed in words, and thus fortunately cannot be recalled. The particular pangs are now forgotten; but the black whirlwind of emotion, the horror of great darkness, and the sense of desertion by God and man, bordering close upon despair, which swept through my mind and overwhelmed my heart, I can never forget, however gladly I would do so. . . .

From all this anguish I should of course have been saved had

I been rendered insensible by ether or chloroform, or otherwise, before submitting to the operation. . . .

But there are other modes in which anaesthetics may serve a patient than by rendering him insensible at the period of his undergoing a surgical operation, and it is to these modes of service, which may not strike even the most humane and thoughtful surgeon, and cannot be matters of experience except to patients who have not taken anaesthetics, that I seek mainly to refer in this letter. . . .

I belong, . . . , to that large class, including most women, to whom cutting, bruising, burning, or any similar physical injury, even to a small extent, is a source of suffering never willingly endured, and always anticipated with more or less of apprehension. Pain in itself has nothing tonic or bracing in its effects upon such. In its relation to the body, it is a sheer and unmitigated evil, and every fresh attack of suffering only furnishes a fresh proof of the sensitiveness possessed to pain, and increases the apprehension with which its attacks are awaited.

When I, accordingly, made up my mind to submit to the operation proposed to me, it was with the fullest conviction that the pain it would occasion would far exceed my power of patient tolerance, and I prepared for it, simply as for a dreadful necessity from which there was no escape. I awoke each morning from troubled sleep to reconsider the whole reasons for and against submitting to the surgeons, and by a painful effort reached again the determination not to draw back from my first resolution. From all this distracting mental struggle, which reacted very injuriously on my bodily constitution, I should have been exempted, had I been able to look forward to the administration of chloroform. . . .

Further; during the operation, in spite of the pain it occasioned, my senses were preternaturally acute, as I have been told they generally are in patients in such circumstances. I watched all that the surgeons did with a fascinated intensity. I still recall with unwelcome vividness the spreading out of the instruments; the twisting of the tourniquet; the first incision; the fingering of the sawed bone; the sponge pressed on the flap; the tying of the blood-vessels; the stitching of the skin; and the bloody dismembered limb lying on the floor.

Those are not pleasant remembrances. For a long time they haunted me, and even now they are easily resuscitated; and though they cannot bring back the suffering attending the events which gave them a place in my memory, they can occasion a suffering of their own, and be the cause of a disquiet which favours neither mental nor bodily health. From memories of this kind, those subjects of operations who receive chloroform are of course free; and could I, even now, by some Lethean draught erase the remembrances I speak of, I would drink it, for they are easily brought back, and they are never welcome.

. . . That the dread of pain keeps many a patient from submitting to operations, which would save life, is notorious, . . .

. . . Before the days of anaesthetics, a patient preparing for an operation, was like a condemned criminal preparing for execution. He counted the days till the appointed day came. He counted the hours of that day till the appointed hour came. He listened for the echo on the street of the surgeon's carriage. He watched for his pull at the door-bell; for his foot on the stair; for his step in the room; for the production of his dreaded instruments; for his few grave words, and his last preparations before beginning. And then he surrendered his liberty, and revolting at the necessity, submitted to be held or bound, and helplessly gave himself up to the cruel knife. . . .

Further; the horror with which attached relatives regard the prospect of operations on those very dear to them; a horror far surpassing that with which they would, in many cases, hear of such operations awaiting themselves, leads them often to dissuade their friends from submitting to surgical interference. The issue in too many cases is, that the poor patient listens, though but half convinced, to their arguments; tries doctor after doctor, and remedy after remedy, only to be compelled in the end, after weeks or months of prolonged suffering, to submit to the operation. . . .

The sum you will perceive of what I have been urging is, that the *unconsciousness* of the patient secured by anaesthetics is scarcely less important than the *painlessness* with which they permit injuries to be inflicted on him. To steep his senses in forgetfulness, and throw the whole intellectual machine out of action, when if allowed to work, it only moves with a rapidity and irregularity which threaten its integrity, and permanently injure it, is to do him a service, second only to that of saving him from suffering. And to make it impossible for him to recall a scene of horror, and torture himself by going over and over all its incidents again and again, is also to do him a signal service. Nor need more be said concerning the service done to his friends.

I plead therefore for the administration of anaesthetics on the grounds enumerated. I fear you may think my confessions exaggerated, but I can most honestly declare that they are not. When I first heard that anaesthetics had been discovered, I could not and would not believe it. I have since thanked God many a time, that He has put it into your heart, and into that of other wise and humane men, to devise so simple and so safe a way of lessening pain.

As for the fear entertained by some, that the moral good which accrues from suffering, and is intended by the Ruler of all to be secured by it, will be lost if agony is evaded by sufferers having recourse to anaesthetics, we may surely leave that to the disposal of Him who does all things well. The best answer to such complaints I have heard, was that given by an excellent old lady to another, who was doubting whether any of the daughters of Eve were at liberty to lessen by anaesthetics the pangs of child-bearing: 'You need not be afraid,' said the wiser lady, 'that there will not be enough of suffering in the world.'

I think not; but you may be honoured still further to reduce its sum.——

LETTER FROM 17 BUFFALO PHYSICIANS

During the winter term of 1849/50 Dr. James P. White, Professor of Obstetrics at Buffalo Medical College demonstrated, for the first time in America, a woman in labor before medical students. An editorial in the *Buffalo Medical Journal*, commenting favorably on "The illustration of labor with the living subject," as a practice which, "although doubtless a novelty in this country . . . enters, however, into the instruction of some foreign schools," elicited the following angry rejoinder from seventeen indignant Buffalo physicians.

To Dr. Austin Flint, Editor, the *Buffalo Medical Journal*

Buffalo, Feb. 21, 1850

The undersigned, members of the Medical Profession, have noticed with regret, in the February number of your Journal, the Editorial article, and the correspondence to which it refers, entitled "Demonstrative Midwifery."

The propriety of the exhibition with the living subject, before the graduating class at the College, as we understand it, does not, in our view, admit of a public discussion; and our only object in this communication is to say, that the practice does not "commend itself to the cordial approbation of the medical profession" of Buffalo, but on the contrary merits a severe rebuke; because we deem it wholly unnecessary for the purpose of teaching, unprofessional in manner, and grossly offensive, alike to morality, and common decency. For the credit of the medical impostors. And this is so enormous, that it is not to be peated in this, or any civilized community.

WILLIAM MATTHEWS

If we may believe the writer of the following letter, an early graduate of Rush Medical College in Chicago, the standards of medical practice in the American Midwest in the 1840's were far from satisfactory. Quacks, it seems, abounded and found great favor in the eyes of the population which, in this respect, did not deviate much from a frequently observed pattern.

To John McLean, M.D.

Eberle, Ind., March 1, 1849

You will probably recognise in my name that of one of the Graduates of Rush Medical College, Session '47-8. . . . my object in writing you is . . . to give you some account of the state of Medical Science here in Indiana. Long shall I cherish those affectionate feelings for the Profesors of the College, contracted in the course of a few weeks' intercourse nor can I ever repay them for a moiety of the benefits which by application and diligence I was enabled to acquire from their course of instruction. I will never-the-less, promise *you* to do all the good that I can in my humble way for the advancement and promotion of our noble science. But here I find little to encourage me to persevere in the investigation or any literary undertakings here, (and I presume it is the case everywhere), I have to contend with Quacks, both in and out of the profession. It does appear to me that the people love to honor quacks and reward them for their ignoble qualities. Here, it is not uncommon for a lazy, worthless, and it may be, dishonest drunken *boy*, destitute not only of education, but even of common sense, to loiter about someone's office,—a quack, too, it may be,—for a few months, and then to leave "for parts unknown," and the next account we have of him he is a great doctor away out West. . . .

A few years ago a fellow destitute of education (a blacksmith residing a few miles west of Indianapolis) quitting his trade without further tediousness, became a "Regular Physician" and began to practice. He had presently to dispute the field with a Graduate, a gentleman of fine acquirements and in every way worthy; and although he never studied to improve himself after entering upon a practice, a few years found him retired in possession of a handsome fortune—for he charged heavily— while his gentlemanly and very competent competitor had to seek other employment for means of support. Nor could this man, although he affected to be very learned, spell *sugar* or *grain* or *medicine!* the day he took in his shingle. Ought not such men to be driven from the profession? Ought they to receive, as the one referred to did, the caresses of educated physicians?

The addressee of the above letter was one of the founders of Matthews' alma mater which, established in 1843, had received its name not so much in honor of the "Father of American Medicine" as ". . . in hope of his heirs handsomely remembering it"; as the widow of an original staff member later wrote. The founders had, the lady added, "however, . . . received no more than a letter of thanks."

JAMES HINTON (1822-1875)

An idealist with a high ethical opinion of the practice of medicine James Hinton, like many another physician, early became disillusioned. After being in practice for two years he wrote to his fiancée.

To his fiancée

March, 1852

I must confess that I ought to be busier, and I will try and find out some way of becoming so. I must cause people to hear of me, not as a clever theorist or a successful investigator of science, but as a very excellent hand at the actual cure of diseases. That is the only thing people care about, and perhaps rightly. But the great thing that takes with them is the puffing off of some new or peculiar mode of treatment. That is the essence of quackery—*and that's what pays.* . . .

And somewhat later he wrote to her:

April 1852

I do believe the difficulties under which I labour at present are necessary for me, absolutely necessary to make me give my mind, as people say, "to business." For, in spite of reason and right feeling, &c., doctoring, like preaching, is become in these

days a trade, and must be carried on like *a trade* if it is to produce a living, and the sooner I am brought to feel and submit
to that the better. I have made up my mind to it now. I fully
perceive and understand that the part I have to act by my
profession is not to do my best for *it* but for myself. I must make
it yield me, in the first place, tables and chairs and house,
butcher-meat and bread, a good coat and a gold watch, and then
I may seek from it scientific and philosophical pleasure, moral
elevation, the happiness of doing good, &c. I perceive and assent.
I suppose, in fact, it is right and necessary—the best upon the
whole. But nothing but a considerable amount of pressure
would have brought me to this view. If I had had but a little
money and not been compelled to earn every penny, I should
never have made a farthing. But at the same time, if I had
thought that in Canada I could have practised my profession,
as a MAN and not as a trader, I should have been much more
willing, if not absolutely inclined to go there.

Later Hinton became the foremost specialist in his field
(surgery of the ear) and a very highly paid physician. And then
at the height of his career, at the age of fifty-one, he retired
from the practice of medicine.

Among the letters written to his future wife many years earlier
are two which are as pertinent today as they were then.

August 1850

I may perhaps as well tell you a little more plainly, the nature
of the objection entertained by the profession against Mr. ——
(not Dr.); I do so, not on his account at all, but because it may
serve to render clear to you a principle of wide application, which
the public seem to find it very hard to understand, but of which

it is desirable that you, as a medical man's wife, should have a comprehension.

In the first place, it is not an objection to the remedial means he employs; secondly, it is not that they deny the cures he has effected; thirdly, it is not jealousy of his success, or a wish to underrate his merits; the matter is simply this—it is a universally recognised law among the members of the profession that all improvements or inventions are the common property of the entire body, and are never to be held as secrets for the aggrandisement of one individual. Is not the reasonableness of this rule on the score of *humanity*, to say nothing of other reasons, manifest?

Again, it is a rule that the profession, and not the public, are the proper judges of the value of any remedy, whether new or old; and that the public opinion in favour of any is not to be sought except as the *results* of practice, and the testimony of the profession may silently and gradually ensure it. The reasonableness of this rule also, though perhaps not quite manifest to you, is evident enough to any person who knows the deceptiveness of limited experiments, and the deceivableness of mankind.

Hence, you will perceive that any person who chooses to break these rules, voluntarily and deliberately, and for the sake of some gain, which is usually obtained, puts himself beyond the pale of the profession. The public think he is an extraordinarily clever person, his brethren call him a quack. In this it is quite clear there is no hardship. A man has a choice of keeping his character, perhaps at the sacrifice of some possible pecuniary emolument, or of sacrificing it for the sake of increased receipts. Tastes may differ as to the proper course to be pursued; but it is evident that a man cannot sell his character, and keep it too.

You perceive, therefore, that for a man to take out a patent for any supposed improvement in medicine or surgery; or to advertise that he is able to cure any disease better than other medical men, is to make himself a quack. Mr. —— has done both, and in his case, as it almost invariably does in the present state of ignorance among the people, it has paid him well. No doubt he can afford to laugh at more scrupulous people, but for my own part I sincerely hope that if ever I do such a thing I may be made a beggar through it.

After hearing such remarks as I have made above, people might say, That is all very well, but what is it to us? If there is a man who can cure us, what difference does it make to us whether he advertises or not, or why should we stop, before having recourse to him, to ascertain whether he complies with the regulations of the profession? The reason for it is this, that every individual has a direct and immediate interest in the honour and integrity of the entire body of medical men. It should never be forgotten that when a sick person employs a doctor, he of necessity places his health, and perhaps his life, absolutely in his hands, and has no manner of security against their being tampered with except in the *character* of the individual. He cannot judge whether his modes of treatment are right or wrong, or at least only too late to be of any service to him, and the only precautions he can take are two—First, to be careful in the selection of his own adviser; and second, but not less important, to do all in his power to maintain a high moral tone throughout the body—or at any rate to let whatever influence he does exert be in that direction.

Now I need not point out to you that any man who employs a quack exerts his influence in precisely the opposite direction. Every shilling which is so spent goes to swell the aggregate of a fund which is acting as a perpetual temptation to medical men to betray their consciences, viz., the income enjoyed by medical impostors. And this is so enormous, that it is not to be wondered at that men are continually to be found who accept the bribe; but the guilt, or at least the folly, lies almost as much with those who offer it. . . .

December 1850

Indeed, dearest, your health is the great thing for you to attend to now, because that has already been much tried, and if you have to live in the heart of London all your days, you will want a stock of health to bear it. You know, I am naturally anxious about health, because I see so much sickness, and because I know how apt good people like yourself are to let themselves be over-excited until their strength is exhausted, and the occupations of life become a burden to them. It might do you good to know a little more of A——, for then you would see an illustration of the moral evils which come in the train of what seems like a venial (perhaps even praiseworthy) disregard of health.

I have a right to speak on this subject. I am myself an instance of it. I labour now under, and shall always, I fear, retain, an irritability of temper caused absolutely and only by my foolish trifling with my health in bygone days, when I used to waste the time necessary for sleep in abortive efforts to study.

So inconsistent are mankind (such good friends to doctors by the by) they ill-use their poor bodies most cruelly, most wickedly; they treat them as a boy does a plaything; sacrifice their well-being to every idle whim of the mind, and every low caprice of the appetite. If they are remonstrated with they will pay no heed; they say, "Oh, I am very well," or "I am never accustomed to think of my health," or "I don't believe this will hurt me." They will go yet further; they will shut their eyes to the plainest indications of suffering health; they will not notice little ailments; they will think they are nothing and persist in all their evil practices, and all their friends encourage them; until at last the mischief gets a little worse, they become what they call ill, and all is terror and distress. A fuss is made, as unreasonable as the former neglect. Everything is sacrificed to this once-despised health, and yet when it is regained, it is only to be again trifled with in like manner. Is it not a true picture, dear? Mayn't a man whose constant occupation is among such scenes be excused for feeling and speaking strongly about it? . . . .

SIR WILLIAM T. GAIRDNER (1824-1907)

The bantering tone of the following letter should not deceive us that the writer was not very much in earnest. William Gairdner, a young Scottish physician who later rose to eminence in his profession, touches in this letter upon an aspect of medical practice about which most laymen are poorly informed: the question of the remuneration of the physician. Engaged in one of the most responsible and exacting professions, the physician has, naturally with exceptions, usually been—and in many countries still is—inadequately compensated. The doctors in the fashionable districts and prosperous suburbs of the big cities are not the measuring rods; those practicing among the less opulent and in the villages and hamlets are the real measure. It is their income that is representative of that of the majority of the profession. In the England of Gairdner's day it was often a mere pittance.

To his brother

November 24, 1854

Many thanks for your kind congratulations and philosophical remarks on the advantages of a Government office over the medical profession. I am not sure, however, that you have quite got to the bottom of the subject. I believe the truth is that the medical profession is supposed by the public to have such fascinations in itself as to repay its cultivators without regard to the filthy lucre, which some of them at least are so lamentably in want of; while you poor devils have nothing but your pay to look for in the way of fun or satisfaction. I don't kick at these arrangements in theory, tho' in practice they are sometimes troublesome to those who, like you and me, require above all things the unrighteous Mammon. It would be the height of absurdity to say that, if this magnificent nation wants a quantity of trifling and fiddle-faddle work done, it should not be paid well for. I think that just as we pay extra for dangerous and unwholesome occupations, so we ought to pay extra for trifles. The more useless the work, the higher should be the pay. Only I fear that on the present system, which admits of unlimited dawdling in our public offices, the idlers would take all the cream, and leave the work to better men. In our profession, though work is often long of reaping its reward, yet it can be said on the other hand that there is no place for the man who won't or can't work. Perhaps, if the rewards were easier got, it would only increase the number of do-nothings—those brilliant and wonderful creatures who seem to be made expressly for bearing off the prizes in every department—queen bees of humanity in everything but that they are utterly barren.

No, I am fully convinced that mankind has just and true instincts in this matter, though the race is not always to the swift or the battle to the strong. I acknowledge, however, that I am sometimes moved to anger, not on my own account, but on that of many poor fellows in medicine, whom I see trusted by the public and toiling out deserving lives among the poor and needy, with no thought for science or art, or for anything except the means of living; scarcely able indeed to eke out a decent income by incessant drudgery. These men, it is true, often disgrace our profession, as in other cases they ennoble it; . . .

JOSEPH STEINER

Childbed fever, the "black death of child bed," as Oliver Wendell Holmes once dramatically called it, every year cost the lives of untold thousands of mothers. Terrifying and mysterious, it unaccountably struck down its victims, who usually succumbed under agonizing symptoms. Many and fantastic were the reasons offered for its explanation when, toward the end of the eighteenth century, British physicians began teaching that it was due to some kind of infection; and in the early 1840's young Dr. Holmes, of Boston, declared flatly that the disease was contagious and was "frequently carried from patient to patient by physicians and nurses." But his was a voice in the wilderness, the most important obstetricians in America declaring the idea preposterous. Holmes did not prosecute it further.

In Vienna, a few years later, another young physician, Dr. Ignaz Semmelweis, independently of Holmes, came to the same conclusions. In meticulous observations on the thousands of deliveries performed yearly in the large lying-in hospital of the Austrian capital, Semmelweis clearly traced the origin of childbed fever to the contaminated hands of the medical students who came from the dissecting room to the hospital wards.

He found credence among but few and even after reducing the number of deaths among the parturients from sixteen in every hundred to one in a hundred he was still declared to be a crank and a crackpot. At first he did not answer his critics, leaving his defense to his medical friends; later he became involved in an acrimonious and distasteful controversy at the height of which he received the following, undoubtedly heartwarming, letter from one of his students. If his contemporaries did not believe him, would the next generation vindicate him?

He was not to know. Cutting his finger during an autopsy, a few years later, he died from blood-poisoning which, ironically enough, is also the cause of death in childbed fever.

To Ignaz Semmelweis, M.D.

Budapest, March 30, 1858

Imbued with the truth of your lectures on puerperal fever, which I had the good fortune of attending during the winter semester, I feel impelled to present some conjectures on how it was possible for all kinds of infections to occur also in the lying-in hospital in Gratz.

During my first surgical semester in Gratz the restaurant of the General Hospital . . . was used by the students as a lounge . . . later when this restaurant was closed they used the dissecting-room for this purpose. Especially the students assigned to duty in the lying-in hospital spent much of their time there. . . . My brother who was then taking a course in practical obstetrics very often came to see me in the dissecting-room; together we studied anatomy on the cadaver or he helped with an anatomical preparation. . . . He would then return to the delivery room. . . . I recall once going to the lying-in hospital with my brother. He put down his hat and cane and proceeded to examine a woman in labor. I asked him why he had greased his hand with fat. "To lubricate it," was his answer. I feel certain that had I seen my brother wash his hand with a liquid (which would have been chloride of lime solution) I should have also wanted to know what it was. But since I hadn't observed anything of the kind I had to believe that my brother had been remiss. His carelessness was, however, predicated upon total ignorance of the cause of puerperal fever. By the same token one may take it for granted that all students assigned to duty at the lying-in hospital are equally negligent. ... The students who are in the dissecting-room frequently therefore present a great hazard for the lying-in women. ... When they leave the dissecting-room to return to the hospital they let their hands dry in the air or they are dried by being put into their pockets. On arriving at the hospital the students examine the patients with the same carelessness as my brother did. ...

LORD JOSEPH LISTER (1827-1912)

To no single individual does surgery owe more than to Joseph Lister. When he entered this field it was a crude, primitive and hazardous art fraught with danger for the patient and faced by him with great trepidation. In transforming this somber picture Lister became one of the great benefactors of mankind.

Born on April 5, 1827 in Upton, Essex, into an upper middle-class Quaker family, he is one of the most engaging personalities in medical history. Of outstanding intelligence, great personal charm and firmness of purpose, he was modest almost to the point of diffidence. His highly developed sense of moral responsibility appears clearly in a letter written to one of his sisters in 1857. At the time he was a young assistant in Edinburgh and had just performed his first public operations; an ordeal for every young surgeon.

To his sister Jane

March 3, 1857

One hasty line to tell thee how the second set of operations went off. I performed two more on 7th day before the students: one of them an exceedingly interesting case, and also requiring a very ticklish operation, viz., the removal of a rather large tumour from the armpit, from among large and important blood-vessels and nerves. I felt this would be a fair trial of my self-command: for the business was very much more trying than the amputation of a thigh or any other *ordinary* operation. The theatre was again well filled, and though I again felt a good deal before the operation, yet I lost all consciousness of the presence of the spectators during its performance, and did it *exactly* as if no one had been looking on. I feel, I may say, truly thankful I was able to go through it as I did. Just before the operation began, I recollected that there was only one Spectator whom it was important to consider, One present alike in the operating theatre and in the private room; and this consideration gave me increased firmness. . . . I trust I may be enabled in the treatment of patients always to act with a single eye to their good, and therefore to the glory of our Heavenly Father. If a man is able to act in this spirit, and is favoured to feel something of the sustaining love of God in his work, truly the practice of surgery is a glorious occupation. I may say I *never* felt better pleased with my profession than now. . . .

Wound infection with its dreadful sequels, erysipelas, gangrene and blood poisoning, was in those days rampant on surgical wards. A fracture of an arm or leg in which the muscles and skin had been torn, or the amputation of an extremity terminated appallingly often in death. One out of every three operations ended fatally. "The man laid on an operating table in one of our surgical hospitals," wrote the famous obstetrician Sir James Simpson, "is faced by more chances of death than the English soldier on the field of Waterloo."

The cause of wound infection was seen in some property of the air, in some miasma stemming from the patients with gangrene and erysipelas. But the surgeons saw no way to combat these conditions and Lister had no clearer concept than anyone else.

His great inspiration came when, in 1865, he became acquainted with the brilliant researches in which Louis Pasteur had shown that fermentation and putrefaction were caused by micro-organisms. Were micro-organisms possibly also the cause of "hospital gangrene?" Was there any chemical which would destroy them after they had invaded a wound, Lister asked himself? Carbolic acid, he was led to believe, might be such an agent.

On May 27, 1866 he wrote to his father about the first patient, an eleven-year-old boy, treated with this "antiseptic."

To his father

May 27, 1866

There is one of my cases at the Infirmary which I am sure will interest thee. It is one of compound fracture of the leg: with a wound of considerable size and accompanied by great bruising, and great effusion of blood into the substance of the limb causing great swelling. Though hardly expecting success, I tried the application of carbolic acid to the wound, to prevent decomposition of the blood, and so avoid the fearful mischief of suppuration throughout the limb. Well, it is now 8 days since the accident, and the patient has been going on exactly as if there were no external wound, that is as if the fracture were a simple one. His appetite, sleep, etc., good, and the limb daily diminishing in size, while there is no appearance whatever of any matter forming. Thus a most dangerous accident seems to have been entirely deprived of its dangerous element.

Other cases followed: amputations, compound fractures, breast operations. The results were astonishingly good. The mortality of operations was greatly reduced. The incidence of wound infection on Lister's wards became less and less and was gradually practically abolished. He published his results in a series of scientific papers. The reaction to them was not what he had expected. Some of his colleagues attacked his method vehemently, among them no lesser person than James Simpson, the majority ignored it entirely, a few surgeons, primarily in Edinburgh, accepted the new principle. Lister was deeply affected by the animosity and apathy he encountered. Very slowly the tide turned. And when it did and his ideas were finally accepted they revolutionized the practice of surgery. Honors were heaped upon him. He was elected President of the Royal Society, England's most distinguished scientific association, he was knighted, he was raised to the peerage and, when he died, a public funeral service was held for him in Westminster Abbey.

A few years after he had treated Queen Victoria for a very deeply seated abscess in the pit of the arm, doubtlessly a very painful condition, he received the following letter from Sir Henry Ponsonby, the Queen's private secretary. It is not unlikely that this letter was addressed to him not only because he was a very well-known medical figure but because the Queen remembered him as a gentle man who had "most pleasantly performed . . . a most disagreeable duty."

Sir Henry F. Ponsonby to Joseph Lister

Balmoral
June 15, 1875

You are no doubt aware that a Royal Commission is about to inquire into the subject of Vivisection, but some time must elapse before any legislation is attempted.

In the mean while it is to be feared that the unnecessary and horrible cruelties which have been perpetrated will continue to be inflicted on the lower animals.

The Queen has been dreadfully shocked at the details of some of these practices, and is most anxious to put a stop to them.

But she feels that no amount of legislation will effect this object so completely as an expression of opinion on the part of some of the leading men of science who have been accused, she is sure unjustly, of encouraging students to experiment on dumb creatures (many of them man's faithful friends and to whom we owe so much of our comfort and pleasure) as a part of the regular educational course.

The Queen therefore appeals to you to make some public declaration in condemnation of these horrible practices, and she feels convinced that you will be supported by many other eminent Physiologists in thus vindicating the Medical Profession and relieving it from the accusation of sanctioning such proceedings.

To this letter Lister sent the following reply. One may not forget the period at which it was written nor the person whose request he so emphatically declined to comply with.

To Sir Henry Ponsonby

(1875?)

Your letter conveying Her Majesty's desire that I should make some public declaration against vivisection, was placed in my hands on my return from the Continent.

I should deeply regret that I cannot see my way to complying with this request, were I not persuaded that my doing so would not promote the real good of the community, which I know to be Her Majesty's only object in the matter. And I feel bound to endeavour to express shortly the reasons for my opinion.

With this object I can hardly do better than begin by saying that I have myself often performed experiments upon the lower animals, and that if I have been privileged in my professional career to do anything for the good of my fellow men, more is to be attributed to these experiments than to any other work in which I have engaged. When they were performed without chloroform, as has not unfrequently been the case, they have been done at a very great sacrifice of my own feelings; but the greatness of the object in view has appeared to me to over-ride such considerations.

That man is justified in causing the death of the lower animals for his own advantage is allowed on all hands. Animal food is not indispensable to man, as the example of the vegetarians teaches; yet its use is all but universal, and is indeed abundantly sanctioned by Scriptural authority.

The infliction of pain upon the brute creation is also allowed by all to be justifiable when some important human interest is supposed to be served. If, for example, a valuable race horse were affected with a tumour, not growing from any vital part or causing any inconvenience to the animal, but disfiguring it or interfering with its successful running, I doubt whether any one would be found who would object to a veterinary surgeon being called in to remove the growth; although the pain involved in the operation would be inflicted, not for the good of the horse at all, but merely for the sake of the pride or purse of the owner. Or to take another more cogent example, which the great importance of the subject compels me to adduce. All oxen and the great majority of our male domestic animals, such as sheep, pigs, and horses, have been subjected to an operation involving exquisite agony in its execution, and often severe pain from subsequent inflammation in the wound, the object being to make them more easily fattened for slaughter, their flesh more fitted for human food, or in the case of the horse to render them more patient and docile servants. Compared with practices like these, that which has received the odious appellation of vivisection is justified by far nobler and higher objects; not the ministering to the luxury or comfort of a generation, but devising means which will be available throughout all time for procuring the health of mankind, the greatest of earthly blessings, and prolonging of human life.

When therefore I have had placed before me on the one hand the reasonable prospect of promoting these great objects, and on the other my own unwillingness to inflict pain, I have felt bound to give the greater weight to the former.

Anyone who feels it to be his duty to perform such experiments has the comfort of knowing that the sufferings which he causes are not at all to be compared with those which a human being would endure if similarly treated. With regard to this very important consideration two distinct points have to be borne in mind. First, all physiological experience teaches us that the sensibilities of an animal are less acute the lower it is in the scale of creation. Hence we may be sure that the pain felt by frogs, which are by far the most common subjects of experiment, is really of an insignificant and trifling character. Frogs are closely allied in organisation to fishes; and the manner in which a salmon pulls after taking the fly is of itself clear proof that the sensibility of the tongue and interior of the mouth and throat is utterly insignificant compared with that of the same parts in man. Indeed were this not the true state of the case it would surely be unjustifiable to engage in trout or salmon fishing, or to catch sea fish with the long line, to which they remain attached for hours together after they have taken the hook. And for those who have no objection whatever to fish being caught in these ways to raise an outcry against scientific experiments upon a few frogs seems to me, I confess, simply ludicrous.

Secondly, with regard to animals such as dogs or rabbits which, being much higher in the animal scale than frogs, are undoubtedly endowed with correspondingly keener sensibility, it is to be remembered that absence of the faculty of reflection in the lower animals, and the comparatively instinctive character of their mental operations, save them from a great deal of the torment which men endure. They know nothing of the agonies of anticipation which, when surgical operations are performed without anaesthetics, are often far worse than the actual pain caused by the knife. Even during the performance of the experiment the sufferings of the lower animals are as it were of a physical or passive nature; since they have not the ability to reflect on and appreciate the horrors of their situation. And no sooner is the actual pain over than the creature, unable to meditate on what has happened, appears perfectly unconcerned and happy; and the story sometimes told of a dog licking the hand of a physiologist in the course of an experiment, is, if properly regarded, much more striking as a proof of absence of suffering in the animal than of cruelty in the physiologist.

Indeed the term cruelty seems to me altogether misapplied in the discussion of this question. An act is cruel or otherwise, not according to the pain which it involves, but according to the mind and object of the actor. If a father chastises a beloved son for his good, he discharges a duty painful to himself but full of kindness to the child; whereas if he were to use the whip or rod in precisely the same manner for the purpose of torturing the boy, he would be one of the greatest of human monsters. Even the fox-hunter is not commonly regarded as cruel; because the protracted bodily suffering of increasing fatigue combined with the utmost mental torture which a fox can be supposed capable of enduring, not to mention the final act of worrying by the dogs, are not the objects which the hunter has in view, but, if he ever thinks of them at all, are regarded as entirely secondary to the gratification of himself and his friends. But surely those who regard this amusement as justifiable are strangely inconsistent if they brand with the epithet cruel the man who performs an experiment upon an animal at great sacrifice to his own feelings and with every care to render the pain as slight as is compatible with the high object in view. And I am bound to add, in vindication of the honour of my own Profession, that medical men are, as I believe, on the average the most humane class of the community, their whole lives consisting in the practice of beneficence in a form which constantly evokes and educates their best feelings. And whatever may be the case in other countries, I feel sure that the avoidance of needless suffering may be reckoned on with entire confidence in the performance of experiments on the lower anmials in Britain.

It is sometimes said that, although such experiments may be needful and right for the purpose of discovery, they are not justifiable for the demonstration of truths already ascertained. It would, I believe, be very wrong to draw any such line of distinction. To take a single instance; to debar the student of medicine from having his eyes opened to the truth of the circulation by seeing the blood coursing through the vessels of the living web of the frog's foot, would be undoubtedly a mistake: for no amount of verbal teaching could do for him what a glance through the microscope at that sight at once effects.

Demonstrations upon the higher and more sensitive animals are, I believe, in this country always made painlessly under anaesthetics; and this is undoubtedly right, in order to avoid the demoralizing effect that might be produced upon the minds of the class and that of the operator himself by the infliction of needless suffering. As regards the pain to the animals themselves it is in sober truth far from being the principal item for consideration.

That which they would experience in such experiments without chloroform would be often much less than they would endure if left to die in the ordinary course of nature from violence or disease, or from cold or hunger; and all the so-called vivisections that take place in a year in Great Britain would, if done without anaesthetics, cause less torture than may result from the winging of pheasants in a single day's sport on the battue system. But the deliberate infliction of needless pain would have a most injurious influence upon those who caused or witnessed it, and it is therefore of the utmost importance that it should be avoided. This however, as I said before, may be safely left to the humane feelings of those engaged in teaching physiology in our medical schools and those members of the profession whom an ardent desire for the pursuit of truth and the benefit of their fellow creatures may urge to prosecute such investigations as private individuals.

I am therefore clearly of opinion that legislation on this subject is wholly uncalled for; while any attempts of that kind might prove very injurious by checking inquiries calculated to promote the best interests of Her Majesty's subjects.

The man who showed such firmness in support of a scientific procedure which, even today, is regarded by many as cruel was the kindest and most considerate of men. On ward rounds Lister once found a little girl weeping bitterly. The child's worn rag doll had ripped open, the sawdust had spilled on the floor and the nurse had taken the doll from her. "The Chief" asked for needle and thread and sitting on the little patient's bed he gravely repaired the damage. And it was probably incidents like this that once prompted a little "street arab" on his wards to remark: "I think it's the little yins and the auld wimmin he likes best."

the most fearfully anxious. I operated on the Countess de F. . . .
Upon Dr. Campbell was imposed the responsibility of the
chloroforming. The operation was begun at 10 o'clock, with the
expectation of its lasting about an hour. Everything went on
well, and in fifty minutes it was nearly finished. There was
nothing to do but to secure the silver sutures. Just then I noticed
a very livid appearance of the tissues, and called Dr. Johnston's
attention to it. I asked if all was right, was answered "Yes, go
on." But almost immediately Dr. Campbell said "Stop a moment.
Let her head hang down." He ordered Nélaton to support the
head, and Johnston to raise her feet perpendicularly in the air,
while he supported the body and shoulders, and Béclard attended
to forcing the respiration by pressing the thorax and abdominal
walls. Young Herbert was sent for a spoon, with the handle of
which her locked jaws were forced asunder, and Nélaton called
for a forceps to pull the tongue from the top of the wind-pipe.
A tenaculum was handed, the tongue hooked up and held
firmly. And I, imagine poor me, standing like a very statue of
sadness and sorrow, calling out mechanically every now and
then, "My dear Dr. Campbell, is there any hope of saving her?"
She was to all intents and purposes dead. They held her in this
inverted position for twenty minutes, trying to force the respira-
tory function. It appeared to me to be useless. At last she
breathed, and breathed again. It was very poor breathing, but
better than none at all. The doctor said: "Don't be alarmed, she
will recover." After a while they laid her on the table in the recumbent posture. But soon, almost immediately, the breathing
ceased again, and the pulse stopped too, as it had done before.
Again they quickly inverted the body, and again long, painful,
protracted and anxious efforts for resuscitation were repeated as
before—but now she seemed more dead than before, and I
thought spontaneous respiration would never again return; but,
thanks to the brave men who had her in charge, for they never

ceased their efforts, and after a seeming very long time, they were repaid by feeble signs of returning life. Respiration had some regularity, the pulse became countable, though very weak and sometimes suspended. My heart began to pour forth involuntary thanks to God for her recovery. They laid her upon the table again, saying, "It will all be right now." But in a few seconds the respiration ceased a third time, her pulse was gone, and she looked the perfect picture of death. Then I gave up all as lost. . . . It seemed to me she would never breathe again, but at last there was a spontaneous spasmodic inspiration, and after a while another, and by-and-by there was a third. They were very "far between." I thought there would never be a fourth one, but there was, and then there was a long yawn or gaping. . . . The operation was finished. It was one of the most difficult I ever executed, and certainly the most difficult, take it all in all, that I ever performed on any one in the upper walks of life. Of course, it is needless to say, it was completed without further recourse to the use of chloroform. . . .

I have given you the facts. I can not and will not try to tell you the heart-rending agony through which I passed during the nearly two hours of anxious, persevering effort for her resuscitation. But the best part of the story is to be told. Although it has been but forty-eight hours since the operation, I am able to pronounce the verdict of a perfect cure.

. . . Tell Emmet I am done with chloroform, will never again operate on any patient under its influence, and believe it ought to be banished from ordinary or general use. It is too dangerous . . . My hands are . . . henceforth, washed of chloroform and devoted to ether. . . .

JOHN G. PERRY (1840-1921)

John G. Perry, a medical student, entered the Union Army as a volunteer contract assistant surgeon in 1862. For more than two years he was in the midst of the fighting. Sometimes with the troops in the field, sometimes in hospitals directly behind the front. A collection of letters written by him during this time was published by his wife forty years later under the title *Letters from a Surgeon of the Civil War*.

To his wife

July 3, 1862

. . . One of my Confederate patients died today. He called me to his bed early this morning and said that he knew of his condition and was fully prepared to go, but there was one thing he wanted to do before the end, and that was to beg me to take his money and buy something which I could always keep in remembrance of him. He talked a great while about it, nor could I persuade him that he ought to divide the whole sum among the nurses who had been so kind to him. At one o'clock he died; you will realize the simple pathos in the last act of this poor fellow's history, when I tell you that his whole fortune amounted to less than fifty cents. . . .

To his wife

Two Miles from Hanover Junction
May 24th, 1864

I can scratch only a few lines, being up to my elbows in blood. Oh, the fatigue and endless work we surgeons have! About one night in three to sleep in, and then we are so nervous and played out that sleep is impossible.

The hospital is fast filling up with poor fellows who last night charged upon the enemy's works on the other side of the river. We are some fifteen miles nearer Richmond than when I last wrote, and the strongest works of the Confederacy are at this point and at the South Anna River. They were thrown up during the first year of the war.

It looks now as if we should still compel the enemy to fall back. We have had a deal of forced marching lately, and the heat has been almost intolerable. At times it has seemed as if the sun's rays would lay us out, yet we march all day, and through volumes upon volumes of dense dust. News has just come that the Confederates are falling back, and so I suppose we must pack our wounded into wagons and move after them with all the speed possible.

It seems to me I am quite callous to death now, and that I could see my dearest friend die without much feeling. This condition tells a long story which, under other circumstances, could scarcely be imagined. During the last three weeks I have seen probably no less than two thousand deaths, and among them those of many dear friends. I have witnessed hundreds of men shot dead, have walked and slept among them, and surely I feel it possible to die myself as calmly as any,—but enough of this. The fight is now fearful, and ambulances are coming in with great rapidity, each bearing its suffering load.

To his wife

Field Hospital near Petersburg
June 24th, 1864

When our division was withdrawn from the extreme front, where it has been since the beginning of the campaign, we surgeons looked for a little less arduous work; but now the artillery brigade has been placed under our care, and we have as much to do as ever. It has not rained for a month, and the poor wounded fellows lie all about me, suffering intensely from heat and flies. The atmosphere is almost intolerable from the immense quantity of decomposing animal and vegetable matter upon the ground. Many of the surgeons are ill, and I indulge in large doses of quinine. Horses and mules die by hundreds from continued hard labor and scant feed. The roads are strewn with them, and the decay of these, with that of human bodies in the trenches, causes malaria of the worst kind.

War! war! war! I often think that in the future, when human character shall have deepened, there will be a better way of settling affairs than this of plunging into a perfect maelstrom of horror.

To his wife

Field Hospital, June 29th, 1864

Rumor says that the Twentieth is to be mustered out of service on the 18th of July.

Grant is winding his forces round Petersburg. Our infantry is about two miles from the Weldon Railroad, and it is reported that our cavalry have cut the railroad lower down. The Confederates are close to starvation, especially the women and children, and yet there is no sign of their yielding.

Our division has again been put in the front line of rifle-pits, and again the poor wounded fellows will be coming in. All this accumulation of experience quickly changes careless boys into sober and thoughtful men,—men who trust, and who feel that whatever happens, in the end it will somehow be for the best; men who value what has not cost them a thought before. I know of a little book, carried in breast pocket or knapsack,—indeed wherever it may seem safest,—that has now become a dependence amid suffering and privation.

MARY PUTNAM JACOBI (1842-1906)

That greatly maligned century, the nineteenth, was in reality one of the most progressive and enlightened in the history of the human race. Its scientific advances were greater than those of any preceding era and its social gains also, were not inconsiderable. Among the latter the beginning emergence of women from their century-old position of inferiority and inequality was especially noteworthy.

Medicine was one of the professions which had been closed to them. Around the middle of the century a handful of women in America and England conceived the unheard of idea of trying to invade this purely male domain. The resistance and opposition they encountered, among the profession and also in lay circles, was formidable. But they were not to be deterred. One of the early intruders into this hallowed preserve was prim little Miss Mary Putnam, a very proper young woman with a delightful sense of humor.

The medical training available to women in the United States in those days was very inadequate. After completion of her studies in this country Mary Putnam went abroad with the hope of being admitted to the famous Medical School of the Sorbonne in Paris. Women had never been accepted there and Dr. Putnam was no more fortunate. She did, however, receive the permission to attend a few lectures and to do some hospital work.

But she did not give up her original idea. When it seemed pretty certain that she would be admitted she wrote to her father that she thought that this was "a great thing for the medical education of all women" and that she felt "singularly honored" that the recognition should have been conferred upon them in her. "I cannot flatter myself," she added, "that it is due to any merit of my own, unless the positive virtue of punctuality in being at the hospitals at half past eight every morning for a year, and the negative one of not flirting with the students, have counted in my favor."

Finally, on January 25th, 1868, she was able to report:

To her mother

Paris, Jan. 25, 1868

Allow me to gratify the anticipation of six months by the following announcement. Day before yesterday, for the first time since its foundation several centuries ago, a petticoat might be seen in the august amphitheatre of the *Ecole de Médicine*. That petticoat enrobed the form of your most obedient servant and dutiful daughter!

I am glad to write you this before I receive what I am daily dreading, your disappointment about the examinations. Admission to the *cours* was all I had really ever dared to hope, and had I followed my own plans, I think that the right to the examinations would have been easily obtained afterwards. I must tell you how I had this—no, I have already written to you how Mme. Garnier invited me to dine with the secretary of Public Instruction, and how, with that practical tact that I am more and more convinced so eminently distinguishes me, (always in spite of the predictions of my friends), I acknowledged the impossibility of opposing the decisions of the Faculty and Academic Council, but proposed to elude them by a demand to assist at the *cours* of a certain professor, Robin, on Histology. How the secretary snatched at this brilliant suggestion, and for a month worked to get it carried out. How I dined a second time with Mme. Garnier, and the secretary told me that the affair was satisfactorily settled. Three days later I received official notice of my authorizations to attend the *cours*. I went, and found that, like all other things, it was as easy as possible, when people refrain from their chronic stupidity: Enter by a side door, separate from the students' entrance, a chair is placed for me in an *enceinte réservée* near the professor, the students, who all know me by sight, do not lift an eyebrow at my appearance, taking it as a matter of course,—I pull out my inkstand and take my notes, and feel as much at home as if I had been there all my life. But in spite of this calm and ordinary appearance, the affair is a considerable triumph. It is practical stratagem executed upon the Faculty, whose lines have been turned by an adroit manoeuvre; and a practical refutation of the humbug that I have heard repeated on all sides, "a woman could not enter the amphitheatre in safety, so great would be the *tapage* among the students, so impossible the efforts of the professor to screen her from the insult and annoyance." Now I always knew this was humbug, but I wanted to have it demonstrated. . . .

And when three years later she graduated from the Sorbonne the event was of sufficient importance for the Paris newspaper *Le Figaro* and the New York *Tribune* and *Evening Post* to carry news items.

At the stated meeting of the Medical Society of the County of New York, on December 4th, 1871, the President of the Society, Dr. Abraham Jacobi, said:

"Concerning our recent admissions, I have another remark to offer. It is not a small satisfaction to me that, in the year of my presidency, one of the most urgent questions of the day should have been quietly and noiselessly answered. The admission of females into the ranks of the medical profession, or rather

—as their obtaining the degree of M.D. is a matter belonging to chartering legislatures, and their obtaining a practice depends on the choice or prejudice of the public—into existing medical societies, has been decided by you by a simple vote, not attended either by the hisses and clamors of excited young men in medical schools, or by the confusions and derogations of the meetings of a medical association. I think we can say that our action has finally settled a question, the importance of which was recognized by everybody. The vote of the largest society of the kind in the Empire State, and, I believe, in the Union, will have the effect of soothing the passions and levelling prejudices in the circles of the army of medical men, forty thousand strong in the United States, and of raising us in this respect to the standard of European countries. Even the conservative seat of learning, Edinburgh, has admitted women to medical studies. Paris has turned out a woman doctor, who will, I hope, prove none of the least ornaments of this Society, the profession of this city and our common country. . . ."

The "woman doctor" in question was Dr. Mary Putnam. She and Dr. Jacobi met for the first time at this meeting. A year and a half later they were married at City Hall.

RICHARD D. ARNOLD (1808-1876)

Throughout the nineteenth century yellow fever continued to harass the Americas. The suddenness of its appearance, the vehemence with which it struck, the total lack of knowledge of its origin and of its way of spreading made its occurrence the object of widespread anxiety almost bordering on panic.

In 1871 news reached Savannah of an outbreak of the disease in Charleston, some eighty miles away. A letter by Dr. Richard Arnold, long a leading physician and prominent citizen of Savannah (he had been mayor for six terms), conveys vividly the fears of the citizenry and the helplessness of the medical profession.

To Meredith Clymer, M.D.

Savannah, Georgia
October 11, 1871

. . . There was a great panic here on the occurrence of Yellow Fever in Charleston. Since our devastating epidemic of 1854, the people at large have turned fools as to the contagion of yellow fever, and I have no desire of stemming the popular torrent. I began to appreciate the good sense of the Old Churchman "Si populus vult decipi—decipiatur." Asses that believe in the tidal wave and the honesty of Ulysses Grant ought to be left to chew their thistle unmolested by argument. My friend the mayor, Col. John Screven, sent for me to advise with, on the first official notification of the appearance of the disease in Charleston. The old women in breeches were frantic and shrieking for stopping the cars between this city and Charleston. I told him that even I, with my positive convictions as to the nontransmissibility of the disease by person or luggage, if acting Mayor, would feel myself compelled to yield to such universal prejudice. But, I said, the best quarantine is Hygiene. Acting on this hint, he took measures to make Savannah as clean a city as can be found anywhere. Privately I expressed my opinions freely, so as to allay Panic. I began the study of medicine in 1826, just six years after our noted Epidemic of 1820. My Preceptor was Dr. Wm. R. Waring, who had been through the whole Epidemic.

At that time you could not have found a solitary Doctor in Savannah who would not have hooted at the idea of contagion. Yellow Fever appeared here in 1827. There had not been a vessel of any kind in Port for several months. This was before the days of Rail Roads and Steamers. Cotton was transported by river. Rivers dried up in the summer. Hence business was suspended entirely from the middle of July up to the beginning of October. No chance for any long, low decked schooner to bring the disease from the West Indies, hidden under peel of a banana or an orange, or lurking in the refreshing juice of a lime as one skillfully mixed it with the grateful Santa Cruz.

No one ever then doubted its local origin.

. . . In 1854, thousands left our plague stricken city carrying carpet bags, bandboxes, trunks, etc. etc. Many died after leaving, from the disease contracted in the city, scores had the genuine disease when away, yet never has there been known a solitary instance of propagation of the disease outside the limits of the City. Just after the Epidemic of 1854, I challenged the proofs of any such transmission of the disease.

. . . The causation of the disease is an intricate subject not susceptible of a very satisfactory solution.

. . . I hope you will tolerate this rather long letter. Fever has been a subject of great excitement here. We have not had a soli-

JEAN CRUVEILHIER (1791-1874)

In reply to a request from a group of country doctors for an expression of his views on the "moral and material interests" of the medical profession, Cruveilhier, the famous Paris pathologist, sent the following letter:

Paris (undated)

... Our profession is one of self-denial, of devotion, of sacrifice: it is truly a ministry. You are aware of this more than any one else, you, my colleagues in the country, whose days and nights are dedicated to the alleviation of suffering humanity and who never deny your help neither day nor night, without worrying about whether your labors will be rewarded. "My best patients are the poor," said the great Boerhaave, "because the Lord has taken it upon Himself to pay me for them." ...

ROBERT KOCH (1843-1910)

Toward the end of April, 1876, Dr. Ferdinand Cohn, Professor of Botany in the University of Breslau, Germany, received the following letter:

To Professor Ferdinand Cohn

Wollstein (Province of Posen)
April 22, 1876

Stimulated by your investigations on bacteria which were published in the "Beitraege zur Biologie der Pflanzen" I have occupied myself, since I was on several occasions able to procure the necessary material, for some time with the contagious principle of anthrax. After many unsuccessful experiments I have at last succeeded in establishing fully the life cycle of Bacillus anthracis. On the basis of a large series of experiments I believe to have placed the results of my investigations on a sufficiently solid foundation. However, before publishing my results, I very humbly beg you, highly esteemed Herr Professor, to give me your opinion of them since you are the greatest authority on bacteria. I am, to my regret, not able to prove my point by presenting slides containing the individual stages of development since I didn't succeed in preserving the bacteria in appropriate media. I therefore very humbly beg you to permit me to demonstrate to you, possibly at the Institute for Plant Physiology, over a period of several days the most necessary experiments. Should you, highly esteemed Herr Professor, deign to grant this most humble request I would ask you to kindly determine when I should come to Breslau.

With the expression of high regard, yours devotedly

Dr. Koch, District Health Officer.

Professor Cohn had never heard of the writer. Nevertheless he invited him to come and a few days later Dr. Koch arrived with his vials and chemicals, his rabbits, mice and frogs, and he even brought along his microscope.

What Dr. Koch had to show made a profound impression on Professor Cohn and his medical colleagues, one of whom enthusiastically said: "I think this is the greatest discovery ever made in bacteriology and I believe that Koch will some day surprise and shame us all with further discoveries." A prophesy which indeed came true.

Robert Koch, the object of such admiration, was a thirty-three-year-old country doctor who, without the benefit of a scientific institute or of any outside advice had devised in his small improvised laboratory (separated from the rest of his consultation room only by a curtain) an ingenious method for the cultivation of bacteria.

Despite the great promise of this achievement and the continued efforts of his new-won friends to find adequate research facilities for him, Koch had to continue working under the same primitive conditions. In 1879 the medical faculty of the University of Breslau recommending him for an appointment wrote to the Minister of Education:

To the Minister of Education

Breslau, Jan. 17, 1879

The undersigned faculty very humbly takes the liberty of drawing the attention of your Excellency to a man who has, through his excellent investigations on bacteria, decisively furthered the important chapter on the origin and propagation of infectious diseases and who has made for himself a name of high esteem in scientific circles. He is the Royal District Health Officer, Robert Koch, M. D., in Wollstein (Province of Posen).

Under the most difficult external conditions, without personal contact to men of his special field of science, he has without help worked his way up. Unquestionably, a man of such caliber would develop still more profitably within the frame-work of a university; on the other hand, it is to be feared that the necessity of securing one's livelihood which is especially difficult and time and strength consuming in a small community, will curtail and possibly stymie the scientific achievements Dr. Koch is clearly destined to make. . . .

The faculty then proceeded to "most obediently" beg his Excellency to appoint Koch to head an institute which was about to be newly created.

He didn't get the post.

Finally he was given a full-time research appointment which had long been his due. It became the starting point of one of the most brilliant careers in modern medicine in the course of which Koch and his co-workers discovered, within a few years, the germs which cause such prevalent infectious diseases as tuberculosis, cholera, typhoid fever and diphtheria. Koch also proved that wound infection was of bacterial origin thus clinching Lister's earlier intuition.

THEODOR BILLROTH (1829-1894)

There is much talk (among laymen) of the elation physicians must experience in the pursuit of their profession, of the gratefulness of patients and of the gratification physicians doubtless derive therefrom.

Here is what Theodor Billroth, one of the outstanding physicians of his day, a man who had risen to the top of his profession, had to say about these things.

In answer to a relative, whose son wanted to become a physician and who had written to him asking his opinion about the advisability of the young man doing so, Billroth wrote:

To a relative

Vienna, May 4, 1883

. . . if I had a son I should be greatly upset if he wanted to study medicine.

Medicine is a difficult, strenuous, rarely thankful profession, leading only slowly to independence. When I consider how many talented young men there were among my fellow-students and how few of them were really successful, I must say that I was indeed very fortunate. Whether a physician will be successful depends almost more upon his personal characteristics than upon his knowledge, and often enough we see that in this respect his personality plays a greater role than his knowledge and proficiency. . . .

It seems that the young man and his father were not greatly convinced by what Billroth had to say about the chances of a man being a success in medicine. The father, a country squire, wrote a second letter to which Billroth sent the following reply:

To the same

Vienna, Sept. 19, 1883

. . . You write of the farmer's hardships, of his dependence upon the weather, fire, etc.—well, I don't want to scare you and Robert; but the physician, also, is really not 'bedded upon roses'. Competition is becoming ever greater, the start is usually quite difficult. During our student years we probably enjoy acquiring some insight into Nature and the diseases by which man is plagued. After passing our exams we are quite delighted with ourselves, only to realize gradually how fragmentary our knowledge is, how frequently we cannot help where we would most want to help; also, scruples arise as to whether we should do this or that. If we don't want to run around in continual 'Katzenjammer' we have to always tell ourselves that we are doing our duty as best we can. A good, calm wife and tranquil domestic happiness is now the greatest blessing. But hardly at home, hoping to enjoy this happiness, somebody may again knock at our door; duty may call us out into the stormy, cold night. The joys of the physician are scant: here and there a patient's faithful attachment; occasionally, but not often, with pecuniary reinforcement; gratefulness for the utmost fulfillment of duty, even for sacrifices, is rare. The satisfaction of having achieved a successful cure, the consciousness of having done his duty: that is generally the most a physician can attain.

You may feel that I am painting too sombre a picture; however, should Robert happen to come upon these lines in twenty years, he may possibly say that I am right. Should he have a strong inclination to become a physician, nothing ought to daunt him. Don't fear that I shall continue in this vein; the worst has been said and, after all, things aren't much worse than in other vocations.

HENRY INGERSOLL BOWDITCH (1808-1892)

Henry Ingersoll Bowditch, a contemporary of James Jackson, Jr., and like him a graduate of Harvard Medical School, settled in Boston after his postgraduate work in Paris. He spent his long life in Boston where he played a prominent role in medical circles. A man of liberal convictions, he was in the years before the Civil War a well-known abolitionist. Like other broad-minded physicians he favored equal rights for women in medicine. Although the New York County Medical Society had admitted women physicians to membership in 1871, the Massachusetts Medical Society held out for almost another decade and a half. When this society finally voted to admit women, Bowditch, then a man of seventy-six, wrote to an opponent of the measure:

To a physician

Boston, June 29, 1884

You could not have been more surprised than I was at the result of the voting in the M.M.S. It only proves the truth of Emerson's (I think) remark: "Even one is a majority with God on his side." You quote C—— as an opponent. He has been for months one of the most efficient defenders of the propriety of admitting women to the M.M.S.

Suffolk County, while better than it was, has governed the Massachusetts Medical Society, and has had to succumb to the honest thought and love of fair play evinced by the country. The arguments used by —— and —— and —— were to my mind puerile and absurd; and so they seemed to a majority of the Council. Your argument about women going out of their sphere of motherhood, etc., is perhaps good for women bearing children, but there are many single women. Have they no right to study as they please? Have they not a right to support themselves? What right have you, a man, to prescribe what a woman should do in medicine? What argument against women can be drawn from the fact that quacks are abundant? I see no argument in the suggestion. What we want are educated and honest physicians, male and female. But, try as we will, while human nature exists as now, we shall always have a goodly number of quacks, knaves, and idiots; with a smaller number of the nobler type. The Bible you quote against woman. My dear Doctor, having lived and having felt the damnable influence of proclaiming that Bible "inspiration" supported slavery, I care not a straw for any such argument against women's study of medicine. It seems to me not only wholly wrong, but it brings contempt upon the Bible to quote it for such a purpose. The fact that quackery is rampant, and that we *educated ones* (!) are neglected, seems to me irrelevant as an argument.

The following letter written when he was nearly eighty-one years old shows what a physician of his caliber thought of medicine as a profession. It also gives an interesting picture of some of the great advances made in medicine during the nineteenth century.

To Charles A. Powers, M.D.

Boston, May 9, 1889

It would give me the sincerest pleasure to meet the members of the Hospital Graduate Club, but it is, I think, physically impossible for me to do so at present; and then suppose I did appear among you, what could you do with me save to examine me as a fossil hospital graduate who had been buried more than a quarter of a century before any of you were born into the sacred art of medicine from your various hospitals? Nevertheless, I cannot tell you what delightful associations your letter brought before me of some of the fine souls to whom that hospital apprenticeship introduced me! . . . I perhaps might speak to you of my father in medicine, James Jackson; the wise, careful, kindly and skillful hospital physician and warm friend, who first showed me where and how to feel the pulse fifty-nine years ago. Then, too, who could ever forget the great surgeon, John C. Warren, of that day, who was always cool and collected under all, even the most appalling circumstances; who never made more than one bold incision of the proper depth when he knew that would be enough, instead of torturing a patient and the crowd of students, as one of his colleagues did, by half a dozen cuts, each one of which caused as exquisite suffering as the one bold one of the real surgeon, as Warren was. I never saw his superior in America or Europe. Remember we had no ether then. I forbear to mention the name of one of those bunglers. We had our quiet hours of admiration for the surgical ability of the one, and savage contempt for the presumption and overweening vanity of the other. You know as well as I that hospital "internes" always feel able to criticize severely their superiors behind their backs! It is our time-honored privilege, never to be resigned! But a truce to these thoughts. Let us follow a kindlier strain. How delightfully refreshing come up to me under your invitation the halcyon days of my hospital residence, with all their pleasures and their profits. I sincerely hope that each one of you can gather from the memories of that year of residence as much pleasure as I do now: with just enough and not too much responsibility—fine introduction to the weightier duties of active professional life.

Then and there began a career that has always been to me one of the deepest interest, and which lessens not at all, but rather augments as each year rolls on. I hail with the liveliest joy each new glory of modern, clean, antiseptic surgery. These triumphs, with the fine developments of bacteriology, will mark the century towards its close as anaesthesia marked its earlier times as one of the greatest in the history of our art.

It ought to be a source of infinite joy that we are allowed to live in such a grand epoch, each prepared to do his share of the work coming before mankind. I thank God that now, on the verge of eighty-one years, if some fairy were to give me the power of selecting again my career in life, I would select our dear and noble profession before all others the world could offer; feeling assured that by so selecting I should be more certain of a true development, intellectually, morally, and physically, than by any other course I might follow. Let me terminate my letter as I began it, with thanks to one and all of the club. Let us all ever honor our profession, and by our own conduct in connection with one another and with the outside world, make our art in the eyes of all beholders more and more beautiful as a means of alleviating human suffering, and of developing in ourselves all the finer traits of human character.

I bid Godspeed to your club.

Fraternally yours,

Henry I. Bowditch.

THOMAS HENRY HUXLEY (1825-1895)

To the Lord Mayor of London

Monte Generoso, Switzerland
June 25, 1889

I greatly regret my inability to be present at the meeting which is to be held, under your Lordship's auspices, in reference to M. Pasteur and his Institute. The unremitting labours of that eminent Frenchman during the last half-century have yielded rich harvests of new truths, and are models of exact and refined research. As such they deserve, and have received, all the honours which those who are the best judges of their purely scientific merits are able to bestow. But it so happens that these subtle and patient searchings out of the ways of the infinitely little—of the swarming life where the creature that measures one-thousandth part of an inch is a giant—have also yielded results of supreme practical importance. The path of M. Pasteur's investigations is strewed with gifts of vast monetary value to the silk trades, the brewer, and the wine merchant. And this being so, it might well be a proper and graceful act on the part of the representatives of trade and commerce in its greatest centre to make some public recognition of M. Pasteur's services, even if there were nothing further to be said about them. But there is much more to be said. M. Pasteur's direct and indirect contributions to our knowledge of the causes of diseased states, and of the means of preventing their recurrence, are not measurable by money values, but by those of healthy life and diminished suffering to men. Medicine, surgery, and hygiene have all been powerfully affected by M. Pasteur's work, which has culminated in his method of treating hydrophobia. I cannot conceive that any competently instructed person can consider M. Pasteur's labours in this direction without arriving at the conclusion that, if any man has earned the praise and honour of his fellows, he has. I find it no less difficult to imagine that our wealthy country should be other than ashamed to continue to allow its citizens to profit by the treatment freely given at the Institute without contributing to its support. Opposition to the proposals which your Lordship sanctions would be equally inconceivable if it arose out of nothing but the facts of the case thus presented. But the opposition which, as I see from the English papers, is threatened has really for the most part nothing to do either with M. Pasteur's merits or with the efficacy of his method of treating hydrophobia. It proceeds partly from the fanatics of *laissez faire*, who think it better to rot and die than to be kept whole and lively by State interference, partly from the blind opponents of properly conducted physiological experimentation, who prefer that men should suffer than rabbits or dogs, and partly from those who for other but not less powerful motives hate everything which contributes to prove the value of strictly scientific methods of enquiry in all those questions which affect the welfare of society. . . .

Distant rumblings of a controversy which, in the coming decades, was to engender much bitter partisanship inside and out of the medical profession: the controversy between those who believe that the community has an obligation to keep "whole and lively" all of its members and those who are opposed to "state interference." In the more than sixty years which have elapsed since the great English biologist wrote the above letter, the controversy has become ever more acrimonious.

OLIVER WENDELL HOLMES (1809-1894)

In reply to an invitation from the New York Academy of Medicine to attend a reception in its new building on November 20, 1890, Dr. Oliver Wendell Holmes sent the following letter. The father of the famous jurist of the same name had occupied for many years an important place in American medicine and letters, and in his long life he had witnessed one of the most remarkable periods in the history of medicine. In his letter, Dr. Holmes touches upon matters which have always greatly concerned the legitimate physician: the intrusion of the quack and the medical sectarian into medical practice and the willingness of the public to put itself into their hands.

1890

. . . Academies have been too often thought of as places of honorable retirement and dignified ease; roosts where Emeritus Professors and effete men of letters, once cocks of the walk, could sit in quiet rows while the fighting, the clucking and the crowing were going on beneath them. No doubt to be a member of the French Academy,—one of the "Forty Immortals" is an honor worth striving for in spite of Pison's epigram. But the Academy which fulfils its true function is a working body. It deals with living subjects; it handles unsettled questions; it sets tasks for its members, and furnishes so far as it can the appliances required for their performance; it offers rewards for meritorious performances and sits in judgment on the efforts of aspirants for distinction. It furnishes the nearest approach we can expect to a fixed standard of excellence by which the work of new hands and the new work of old hands can be judged. It is a barrier, a breakwater against the rush of false pretensions which are constantly attempting to find their way into public confidence.

Nowhere is such a defence more needed than in the sciences and arts which deal with the health of the community. The public is so ready, so eager to be deceived and the traders in deceptions are so willing, so hungry to deceive those who will listen to them that it needs a solid wall of resistance, a close united phalanx of men of recognized sense, knowledge and character to stand against them. The various forms of what I will venture to christen as pseudopathy and pseudotherapy,— though they are known to the public by other names,—can never loosen the hold of the intelligent thoroughbred physician on the enlightened members of society so long as the best heads in the profession are banded together in a noble institution like this Academy. Only let it remain ever steadfast, unmoveable against the recognition of any such pretenders who have no more business in our associations than the astrologer in our observatories, or the alchemist in our laboratories. We look to this great and able body of men to guard the sacred avenues to the temple of science against all worshippers of idols. The Medical Profession will always have to fight against the claims of wrongheaded, and too often dishonest individuals and "schools" as they call themselves. A fraction of every community will always run after the false prophets. There are a certain number of squinting brains, as there are of squinting eyes, among every thousand of any population. There will always be a corresponding number of persons calling themselves physicians, ready to make a living out of them. Long may it be before the wholesome barriers are weakened that separate the thoroughbred and truly scientific practitioner from the plausible pretender with his pseudopathy and his pseudotherapy. . . .

SIR HENRY THOMPSON (1820-1904)

In 1889 Dr. Brown-Séquard, the famous physiologist at the Sorbonne, caused considerable furor by the announcement of the rejuvenating effects he had experienced from injection of extracts from dogs' testicles. The aging scientist, his own "guinea pig," described with true Gallic enthusiasm the remarkable resurgence of his waning faculties: mental and other.

The ultimate outcome of these experiments is astonishing. They were not confirmed by other investigators; the eminent researcher must have become the dupe of his own desires. But he had given direction to investigations from which our present knowledge of the hormones and hormonal glands stems and in the text books he is celebrated as the founder of modern endocrinology.

The following letter by Sir Henry Thompson, an important English surgeon of the day, reflects the impression Brown-Séquard's "discovery" made on his contemporaries.

Rome, April 17, 1890

. . . I have had ever since the first appearance of Brown-Séquards' remarkable paper on the injection of fresh juices from the testicle for the human subject some correspondence with him & a long talk last summer. I have made some experiments & I have just got a letter from him hoping I will call for another talk, which I shall assuredly do. I don't want to say anything about it, yet at any rate. I can't offer any opinion myself in any terms resembling those which some experimenters, expecially the American have expressed respecting it. But I can't doubt B.-S.s' own experience, or some of the results which he appears to have witnessed in the hands of his confrères. He won't make a single experiment himself on any patient; lest he w'd be accused of desiring to obtain fees by the very tempting prospects held forth of his power to rejuvinate the old fellows on the border of the grave, who would give half they possessed for a reprieve! . . .

Cancer has, beyond doubt, increased during the last sixty to seventy years. Many theories have been advanced in explanation of this alarming phenomenon. Most have been discarded. And while many agents have been accused of causing cancer—bacteria, viruses, coal tars, hormones—none have been conclusively proven to be responsible for it.

Some of the earlier theories appear utterly fantastic today. One can hardly believe that floods and polluted rivers and the consumption of too much meat could have been regarded as the cause of cancer. Still such concepts were advanced in all seriousness.

ALFRED HAVILAND

To the Editors of *The Lancet*

July 16, 1890

. . . In conclusion, I will draw attention to some facts which should not for a moment be lost sight of in any investigation carried on with the view of throwing light upon the cause of the local prevalence and the general increase of cancer. . . .

. . . Since 1851, among the most important improvements in agriculture must be ranked the drainage of the land, which has been carried out to an unprecedented extent since then. The effect of these operations has been to drain the land of excessive moisture both completely and rapidly, and at the same time to afford facilities for heavy rainfalls rapidly to affect the watercourses; hence it is a matter of late experience that, since this system of drainage has been adopted, the floods have not only been more sudden and frequent, but their waters have risen higher, and as a natural consequence have covered larger areas. This increase in the number, suddenness, and extent of floods has been coincident with the increase of cancer among females in the flooded areas . . . the watercourses, became more and more polluted, and in too many cases remain so . . . I have said enough to show how our floods have been gradually increasing in suddenness, extent, and foulness during the last forty years, and we all know that cancer has been increasing coincidently, almost *pari passu* with the increase of this flood nuisance . . . Until this growing evil is checked, we may expect the local prevalence and general increase of cancer to continue.

W. GILCHRIST BURNIE

To the Editors of *The Lancet*

Bradford, March 25, 1900

Everything that tends to clear up the etiology of cancer must be of profound interest to the medical profesion. But I think it may well be asked if the impressions—or would it not be better to say guesses—of even the most eminent observers do not as much hinder as promote our knowledge. Especially is this when, as in the case of Sir William Banks and Sir James Sawyer, an attempt is made to blame the consumption of meat for an increase in the cancer rate; without a single experiment or any statistics tending to show that a meat diet produces cancer, or apparently without any regard to the concurrent alterations in the habits of the people. Assuming the fact that cancer in the male is on the increase, is there not more reason to suppose with Mr. Hutchinson that it is due to increased longevity (to which, it is true, increased nourishment may assist) rather than to the

ANONYMOUS ENGLISH PHYSICIAN

The desirability of treating medical questions as "news items" in the daily press has long been a hotly debated issue. Many physicians are opposed to it. They believe that the very nature of medical research, which makes early and preliminary reports to the profession desirable, and the very nature of the daily press, which is geared to the "scoop," the desire to report something "new," make medical problems often inappropriate newspaper material.

In a letter written more than sixty years ago an English physician shows, in connection with Robert Koch's treatment of tuberculosis with tuberculin, the harm done by premature newspaper reporting.

To the Editors of *The Lancet*

December 17, 1890

Is it not time that some sort of protest should be raised against the continuance on the part of our daily newspapers, metropolitan and provincial, of the publication of strictly medical details? No one doubts that the newspaper press is a great and, on the whole, a beneficient institution, possessed of wide-reaching influence; its capacity for good is unlimited, and, for a like reason, it may occasionally produce quite the opposite result. Its liberty, of which we in this country are naturally proud, may through "journalistic enterprise," as it is euphemistically termed, sometimes degenerate into licence. The unbiased observer must have noted during the past few weeks evidences of such retrogression in respect to the discovery of Professor Koch. It was largely the publicity given to his investigations through the lay press that compelled Professor Koch "against his usual custom" to prematurely lay his results before the world, and this seems to be the chief ground for his withholding the nature of the "remedy." Then the world was treated to the textual reproduction in the columns of daily papers (again through the mutual operation of journalistic enterprise) of a technical medical brochure. Next, these same columns were flooded with accounts of the early stages of clinical records of cases treated by the method. Leading articles were penned *ad libitum,* and doctors were invited to give their "views" on the all-absorbing topic. . . . Newspaper editors are credited with great experience in human nature, and I take it that they know the public taste better than any mere outsider; but, nevertheless, one gravely doubts whether the perusal of these medical details at the breakfast table is calculated to sharpen appetite, or improve digestion of more material sustenance. . . .

SIGMUND FREUD (1856-1939)

Despite its many advances during the nineteenth century medicine had progressed but little in the recognition of mental diseases; nor had it learned much of what James Currie had called, a century before, "the influence of affections primarily mental on the corporeal functions." However, an important step forward was made by Dr. Charcot, the famous French neurologist, who suggested that the symptoms of hysteria, a disease then regarded as being organic, were psychogenic.

A young Austrian physician, Dr. Sigmund Freud, who attended Charcot's clinic in Paris during the winter of 1885-86 was deeply impressed by this interpretation. By his championship of Charcot's views on his return to Vienna, he made many enemies among his psychiatric colleagues. Undaunted by this unexpected animosity, Freud continued his studies on hysteria. Step by step he penetrated deeper into the workings of the mind, gradually evolving methods which enabled him to understand the mechanism of the neuroses. And all the while the psychiatrists became more antagonistic.

During these years Freud corresponded regularly with his friend Dr. Wilhelm Fliess, a physician in Berlin, who took great interest in his psychological studies. Of this correspondence only the letters written by Freud are still extant. The following two, which were written while he was in the throes of developing the method he later called "psychoanalysis," afford a fascinating insight into the personality of this great physician.

To Wilhelm Fliess, M.D.

Vienna, 21. 5. 94

. . . I am pretty well alone here in tackling the neuroses. They regard me rather as a monomaniac, while I have the distinct feeling that I have touched on one of the great secrets of nature. There is something comic about the incongruity between one's own and other people's estimation of one's work. Look at my book on the diplegias, which I knocked together almost casually, with a minimum of interest and effort. It has been a huge success. The critics say the nicest things about it, and the French reviews in particular are full of praise. Only to-day I have been looking at a book by Raymond, Charcot's successor which simply quotes me wholesale in the relevant chapter, of course with complimentary acknowledgments. But for the really good things, like the "Aphasia", the "Obsessional Ideas", which threaten to appear shortly, and the coming aetiology and theory of the neuroses, I can expect no more than a respectable flop. This is bewildering and somewhat embittering. There are a hundred gaps, large and small, in my ideas about the neuroses; but I am getting nearer to a comprehensive picture and some general points of view. . . .

To Wilhelm Fliess, M.D.

Vienna, 25. 5. 95

. . . I have had a inhuman amount to do, and after ten or eleven hours with patients I have been incapable of picking up a pen to write you even a short letter, though I had a great deal to tell you. But the chief reason was this: a man like me cannot live without a hobby-horse, a consuming passion—in Schiller's words a tyrant. I have found my tyrant, and in his service I know no limits. My tyrant is psychology; it has always been my distant, beckoning goal and now, since I have hit on the neuroses, it has come so much the nearer. I am plagued with two ambitions: to see how the theory of mental functioning takes shape if quantitative considerations, a sort of economics of nerve-force, are introduced into it; and secondly, to extract from psychopathology what may be of benefit to normal psychology. Actually a satisfactory general theory of neuropsychotic disturbances is impossible if it cannot be brought into association with clear assumptions about normal mental processes. During recent weeks I have devoted every free minute to such work; the hours of the night from eleven to two have been occupied with imaginings, transpositions, and guesses, only abandoned when I arrived at some absurdity, or had so truly and seriously overworked that I had no interest left for the day's medical work. You must not ask me for results for a long time yet. My reading has been following the same direction. I have been greatly interested in a book by W. Jerusalem on the function of judgment, because it contains two of my main ideas, that judgment consists of a transposition into motor phenomena, and that inner perception can have no claim to be "evidential".

I get great satisfaction from the work on neuroses in my practice. Nearly everything is confirmed daily, new pieces are added, and it is a fine thing to feel certain that the core of the matter is within one's grasp. I should have a whole series of most remarkable things to tell you, but I cannot do it by letter and, what with the pressure of these days, my notes are so fragmentary that they would be of no use to you. . . .

GREVILLE MACDONALD (born 1856)

The discovery of bacteria as the cause of many infectious and contagious diseases was rapidly changing medical practice during the last quarter of the nineteenth century. Physicians were beginning to understand diseases which had sorely puzzled medical men less than a generation earlier and they were beginning to devise efficient methods for treating them.

When Dr. Emil Behring, in Berlin, reported at a medical meeting that he and his Japanese co-worker, Dr. Kitasato, had found a treatment for diphtheria and tetanus the enthusiasm of the doctors present is said to have been overwhelming. Dignified men jumped up on their chairs cheering and applauding the speaker.

Some of this enthusiasm is reflected in the letter of an English physician telling of the first time tetanus antitoxin was used in a patient in Great Britain.

To his father

Harley Street, W
9th Nov. 1895

. . . Here is an absolutely true tale, though I cannot recount it in the charming manner of Helen Tirard. . . . She, her husband and family were in Arran for their summer holiday. On one occasion only did they go to church. After a wearisome prayer of an hour the minister concluded by praying for a little boy then dying of tetanus (lock-jaw). So when the service was over, Tirard, thinking that medical science in that land might not be quite modern, went into the vestry and ascertained who the child was. He started off with his wife immediately, and found the cottage two miles away surrounded by women, who told him it was of no use as the child was dead. With some difficulty he persuaded the mother to let him see the patient, whom at first sight he also thought to be dead; but by the use of hot baths, etc., the child was brought to some life again. The case was a true one of tetanus, from which, as you know, hardly anyone ever recovers. But Tirard meant to try. This last summer it had been shown that, by the use of a certain animal substance, in its nature like the diphtheria antitoxin, animals with tetanus may recover; but it had never been used on a human patient in England. The rest of the story was most graphically told; how the telegraph people in Glasgow were persistently worried—one office after another all being in piety closed, as it was the Sabbath; how at last someone was persuaded to send a message to London; and lastly how the telegram just caught the only man in London who had any supply of the remedy. Then, because there was no boat, it could not arrive by post until Wednesday morning. But Mrs. Tirard tackled a Mr. Coats who had a steam yacht and made him get up steam and cross with her husband in a fearful storm to Ardrossan. The child was, one way and another, kept hanging between life and death, until the remedy arrived; the whole island in intensest excitement. But at last the tiny, precious bottle arrived. For another day and night they waited in dread suspense, fearing that he could not live long enough for the antidote to take effect; yet by Wednesday evening he began to mend, and is now alive and in perfect health. Don't you think it a very dramatic story? . . .

ANTON CHEKHOV (1860-1904)

Anton Chekhov was the son of a small shopkeeper in Tagan-
rog, Russia. After completing his studies at the University of
Moscow he established himself as a practicing physician. During
his student years he began writing for various second-rate magazines. From there he went on to journalism and more serious
writing. He soon became very successful and by the time he had
reached his late twenties he had made quite a name for himself
as a writer. Some of his friends felt that he should give up the
practice of medicine and devote all of his time to his literary
work. Chekhov was of different opinion.

To a friend

Moscow, Sept. 11, 1888

. . . You advise me not to hunt after two hares, and not to think
of medical work. I do not know why one should not hunt two
hares even in the literal sense. . . . I feel more confident and
more satisfied with myself when I reflect that I have two professions and not one. Medicine is my lawful wife and literature is
my mistress. When I get tired of one I spend the night with the
other. Though it's disorderly, it's not so dull, and besides neither
of them loses anything from my infidelity. If I did not have my
medical work I doubt if I could have given my leisure and my
spare thoughts to literature. There is no discipline in me.

A decade later Chekhov again stressed how important his medical background had been to him as a writer.

Yalta, October 11, 1899

. . . I have no doubt that the study of medicine has had an important influence on my literary work; it has considerably enlarged the sphere of my observation, has enriched me with knowledge the true value of which for me as a writer can only be understood by one who is himself a doctor. It has also had a guiding influence, and it is probably due to my close association with medicine that I have succeeded in avoiding many mistakes.

Familiarity with the natural sciences and with scientific method has always kept me on my guard, and I have always tried where it was possible to be consistent with the facts of science, and where it was impossible I have preferred not to write at all. I may observe in passing that the conditions of artistic creation do not always admit of complete harmony with the facts of science. It is impossible to represent upon the stage a death from poisoning exactly as it takes place in reality. But harmony with the facts of science must be felt even under those conditions —i.e., it must be clear to the reader or spectator that this is only due to the conditions of art, and that he has to do with a writer who understands. . . .

At the turn of the century German medicine stood in high esteem. From all parts of Europe, and especially from the East, patients put themselves under the care of German specialists. During the last months of his life Chekhov, who was suffering from tuberculosis, was advised to seek help in a German sanitarium. A letter written a few months before his death describes with mild sarcasm, mingled with overtones of hope for recovery, the skepticism of the physician toward the instituted treatment.

(Badenweiler) June 16, 1904

... The German doctors have turned all my life upside down. At seven o'clock in the morning I drink tea in bed—for some reason it must be in bed; at half-past seven a German by way of a masseur comes and rubs me all over with water, and this seems not at all bad. Then I have to lie still a little, get up at eight o'clock, drink acorn cocoa and eat an immense quantity of butter. At ten o'clock, oatmeal porridge, extremely nice to taste and to smell, not like our Russian. Fresh air and sunshine. Reading the newspaper. At one o'clock, dinner, at which I must not taste everything but only the things Olga chooses for me, according to the German doctor's prescription. At four o'clock the cocoa again. At seven o'clock supper. At bedtime a cup of strawberry tea—that is as a sleeping draught. In all this there is a lot of quackery, but a lot of what is really good and useful— for instance, the porridge. I shall bring some oatmeal from here with me. . . .

WALTER REED (1851-1902)

The specter of yellow fever had haunted the inhabitants of the New World since early colonial times, its mere mention spreading trepidation in the hearts of even the staunchest. The memory of the terrible epidemics in Philadelphia, New York and New Orleans was ever fresh, and the occurrence of cases of "Yellow Jack" among the United States troops in Cuba after the Spanish-American War immediately became a matter of great concern to the Army which sent one of its best epidemiologists, Major Walter Reed, to the island.

Despite the great advances made since the researches of Pasteur and Koch in the understanding of infectious diseases, the cause of yellow fever had evaded detection. At the end of June, 1900, Reed and his associates embarked on their investigations of the theory of Dr. Carlos Finlay, a Cuban physician of English extraction, that the disease was transmitted by mosquitoes. In brilliantly conceived and executed experiments, in the course of which doctors and enlisted personnel voluntarily submitted themselves to the bites of mosquitoes infected with yellow fever, Finlay's theory, which till then had met with little approval, was proven to be correct. The way was open to the conquering of the dreaded disease.

Less than six months after work had begun Reed was able to report to his wife:

To his wife

Columbia Barracks, Quemados, Cuba
Dec. 9, 1900

It is with a great deal of pleasure that I hasten to tell you that we have succeeded in producing a case of unmistakable yellow fever by the bite of the mosquito. Our first case in the experimental camp developed at 11:30 last night, commencing with a sudden chill followed by fever. He had been bitten at 11:30 December 5th, and hence his attack followed just three and a half days after the bite. As he had been in our camp 15 days before being inoculated and had had no other possible exposure, the case is as clear as the sun at noon-day, and sustains brilliantly and conclusively our conclusions. Thus, just 18 days from the time we began our experimental work we have succeeded in demonstrating this mode of propagation of the disease, so that the most doubtful and sceptical must yield. Rejoice with me, sweetheart, as, aside from the antitoxin of diphtheria and Koch's discovery of the tubercle bacillus, it will be regarded as the most important piece of work, scientifically, during the 19th century. I do not exaggerate, and I could shout for very joy that heaven has permitted me to establish this wonderful way of propagating yellow fever. It was Finlay's theory, and he deserves great credit for having suggested it, but as he did nothing to prove it, it was rejected by all, including General Sternberg. Now we have put it beyond cavil, and its importance to Cuba and the United States cannot be estimated. Major Kean says that the discovery is worth more than the cost of the Spanish War, including lives lost and money expended. He is almost beside himself with joy and will tell General Wood when he goes to town in the morning. Tomorrow afternoon we will have the Havana Board of

Experts, Drs. Guiteras, Albertini, and Finlay, come out and diagnose the case. I shan't tell them how the infection was acquired until after they have satisfied themselves concerning the character of the case, then I will let them know. I suppose that old Dr. Finlay will be delighted beyond bounds, as he will see his theory at last fully vindicated. 9:30 P.M. Since writing the above our patient has been doing well. His temperature, which was 102.5° at noon, has fallen to 101° and his severe headache and backache have subsided considerably. Everything points, as far as it can at this stage, to a favourable termination, for which I feel so happy.

Reed's gratification can well be understood. His high hopes and elation appear also in the folowing letter:

To his wife

Columbia Barracks
Quemados, Cuba
11:50 P.M. Dec. 31, 1900

Only ten minutes of the old century remain. Here I have been sitting, reading that most wonderful book, "La Roche on Yellow Fever" written in 1853. Forty-seven years later it has been permitted to me and my assistants to lift the impenetrable veil that has surrounded the causation of this most wonderful, dreadful pest of humanity and to put it on a rational and scientific basis. I thank God that this has been accomplished during the latter days of the old century. May its cure be wrought in the early days of the new! The prayer that has been mine for twenty years, that I might be permitted to do something to alleviate human suffering has been granted! . . . Hark, there go

CARL BECK (1856-1911)

In a communication made on December 28, 1895 to the Physical Medical Society of Würzburg, Germany, Dr. Wilhelm Konrad Roentgen, Professor of Physics at the University, told of a "New Kind of Rays" which had the property of penetrating non-transparent solid bodies such as blocks of wood, books, sheets of hard rubber, etc. Since he could not yet define their physical properties, Roentgen suggested calling the rays, for the time being, "X-rays." In a lecture given a month later Roentgen demonstrated a photograph on which there appeared the bones of his own hand; a picture made by exposing his hand to the passage of the rays.

The hearers were enthusiastic and the chairman, a distinguished scientist, predicted that the rays would be of the utmost significance in the natural sciences, and perhaps, also in medicine, a prediction which has come true to the fullest extent.

Writing to a well-known philanthropist a New York surgeon tells of their early use in the diagnosis of fractures.

New York
February 28th. 1901

This book on fractures, which is the first of its kind, since it teaches the conditions in broken bones, as *they are in life,* through the Roentgen rays, is respectfully dedicated to you. The scientific research, which enabled me to write it, was made in St. Mark's Hospital of this City, a small, overcrowded, poor and unsectarian institution. My work was assisted by the nurses of our Training School—consisting of 38 nurses at present. Some of these nurses were so enthusiastic in their work, that they are now able to teach and propagate the main principles of the new revolutionizing science, thereby rendering immense benefit to human sufferers. I dare say, that many poor laborers, suffering from complicated fractures of the bones, who on account of insufficient judgment before the X-ray era would have been cripples, were discharged from this Hospital with normal extremities now. *Accuracy has taken the place of ignorance and doubt, and painful manipulations cease to be necessary for diagnostic purposes.*

EDGAR TREVITHICK

In the second half of the nineteenth century anesthesia and antisepsis placed surgery on a plane undreamt of only a few decades earlier. Surgeons undertook operations which exceeded by far anything even the most skillful would have ever attempted, with results gratifying to the patient and operator alike. In the exuberance and enthusiasm of success many a man doubtlessly became "knife happy" and too often recourse was taken to surgery instead of to conservative treatment. Many doctors (surgeons and non-surgeons) viewed this development with alarm and disapproval.

To the Editors of *The Lancet*

Cheltenham, May 26, 1903

... how often, in his anxiety to make his mark, is the present-day surgeon led to interfere with parts that do not in reality seriously inconvenience the whole? How often are parts rudely interfered with when they are no more than temporarily deranged and would spontaneously return to their normal conditions if only granted a little grace? How often when the arms of death have already unerringly embraced the whole will the surgeon, with worse than blind enthusiasm, embark in extensive predoomed endeavours to rescue the part? The temper of the surgeon of the day appears to be towards challenging the right of physicians to criticise the results of surgery and indignantly resenting any interference at their hands or from anyone ... who

pleads for rational moderation in the matter of operations. . . .
. . . it is my serious belief that . . . "ere many decades have passed away the operating surgeon will be a far less imposing figure than he now is," and I venture in addition this warning, that popular estimation is a treacherous helm and one that is apt to cause its ship to veer widely. And as the public to-day undoubtedly suffers from an excessive antipathy to venesection, so the day may come when we shall see the present excess of all-round surgical interference replaced by an undue and indiscriminate distrust of it, bred of retaliation in the minds of a disabused laity.

Thoughtful physicians are becoming more and more concerned that also in medicine human relationships, following the general pattern of our age, have become more casual and superficial. Nowhere are interest in the individual and the faculty for sympathizing with him of greater importance than in the practice of medicine. Through the ages medical men have agreed that it takes more than professional skill to make a good physician. There must also be human charity and compassion.

The writers of the following letters, a Victorian Britisher and a modern American, separated in time by half a century and in space by an ocean, stressed these aspects of medical practice in almost identical terms.

ANONYMOUS PHYSICIAN

To the Editors of *The Lancet*

Feb. 2, 1904

. . . Some 45 years ago I made the acquaintance in a quiet Scottish village of a man of the highest culture and most courteous manners, with a somewhat wide experience, I have ever known. . . . when I was in the habit of visiting my friend, if I did not find him in the shop (he was not ashamed of the title) we were sure to gravitate to that center. . . . But I wish at this time to recall the shop, not for its esoteric relations but for its exoteric influences. There had his father laboured and there had my friend grown up from boyhood to manhood among his fellow citizens. The shop door was always open and the practitioner's advice, mostly without fee or reward, always ready for the benefit of his neighbours, for the poor as well as for the rich—advice not only professional but as often as not on matters of business and conduct. And so the motto *"Nihil humanum a me alienum puto"* should before all be our motto, a motto as old as the days of Hippocrates. And if so, is there not a considerable risk of our losing hold of the regard and, it may be, the affections of our patients by standing aloof too much from their daily lives and neglecting the exercise of our immediate sympathies for their behoof? As has been so well said by John Brown (it does one good to write that fine, wholesome, common name): "it is not a case we are treating; it is a living, palpitating, alas, too often suffering fellow creature."

And is there not the danger of becoming ultra-scientific over much of our wise friend Gardner's "naturalist" in medicine and too little of the good old-fashioned Samaritan with his supplies of oil and wine ready in his wallet to administer to the weary wayfarer in life's thorny path of sickness and disease. Charity at second hand is a poor substitute for real brotherly kindness. "Mittened cats do not catch mice." In other words, the true healer must not only be skilled in what to do but be thoroughly acquainted with how to do it. And this implies a readiness of hand and a constant seeing and handling of the weapons or the adjuvants with which he is to fight the elements of disorder, derangement, and it may be death. In this age of specialism, with all its blatant victories—victories which I do not for one moment despise—no thinking person can deny that the everyday skill and attention of the humblest practitioner, our Gideon Grays and MacLures, may, like the quality of mercy and the gentle rain distilled from heaven, do a thousand times more for sweetening the lives of humanity at large than all the triumphs of the greatest and mightiest and most successful of our surgeons and physicians.

LOWIS W. PALFREY (1877-1953)

To the Editor of *The New England Journal of Medicine*

Aug. 2, 1951
Boston, Massachusetts

. . . although in the remote past it was only in rare cases that a doctor could feel that he had saved a life or effected a radical improvement in the course of an illness, now such cases are common. . . .

Must we not realize that although the practitioner of a century ago had no aseptic surgery and few drugs except opium and quinine that we consider worth while, his attendance was still in constant demand and was remembered with gratitude?

Clearly there was an intangible something in his service that must not be allowed to lapse and must still be our chief reliance in the considerable proportion of patients to whom no scientific therapeutics can be applied.

An important part of the reason that these older practitioners gave satisfaction approaching that given by applied science today is the fact, which all thoughtful physicians will confirm, that in many if not most cases when a patient calls a doctor it is not because of intolerable present suffering but rather because of *fear*. . . .

This fear, moreover, is commonly combined with a peculiarly oversensitive emotional state. So he consults a doctor as one who, he hopes, will understand his condition, who may perhaps give him something to relieve present discomforts, but, more importantly, who may reassure him against his worst fears or, in any case, give him confidence that everything possible will be done to meet the situation. And is it not probable that the old-time family doctor, except in cases where a modern cure can be promised, filled this role about as well as is done today?

This basic human reaction of craving help in disease has existed since before the dawn of civilization and is obviously the reason for the existence of the medical profession.

. . . Even today, from the patient's viewpoint, when a man who is in a panic because he believes that he is about to die of pneumonia is given convincing assurance that he is mistaken, is that not comparable in value to a cure by penicillin? And when a patient dying of cancer comes to regard his doctor as something akin to a spiritual counselor, is that not professional service of an ageless sort?

Medical schools of today have more than they can do in their four years' course to teach medical science and its practical application in diagnosis and treatment, and so pay little attention to this more personal aspect of practice. Medical meetings are devoted almost purely to advanced science. In fact, it would be difficult to teach the art of medicine in formal courses, yet it seems to me that more reference should be made to it, by example and otherwise, throughout the years of clinical instruction.

Friendliness and human sympathy are still the rule in medical practice, but should not this function of the medical profession be more strongly and repeatedly emphasized?

SIR WILLIAM OSLER (1849-1919)

Sir William Osler, who takes issue with Maurice Maeterlinck in the following letter, was at the time Regius Professor of Medicine at Oxford University. He had come there from Baltimore where he had played an important part in the development of the Johns Hopkins Hospital and Medical School. A man of high intelligence and wide learning which extended far beyond his immediate field, he exerted great and lasting influence over his contemporaries to many of whom he was their hero. It is undoubtedly no exaggeration to say that he was the most prominent Anglo-Saxon internal medical man of his day.

His thoughts on the physician's role in helping the dying are a tribute to his great humanity.

To the Editor of *The Spectator*

Christ Church, Oxford
Nov. 4, 1911

A student for many years of the art and the act of dying, I read with eagerness Maeterlinck's recent Essay, only, I must confess, to be disappointed. A brilliant example of the type of literature characterized by Hamlet in his famous reply to Polonius, there is an unpleasant flavour, a cadaverous mustiness about the Essay which even the words cannot cover; and in spite of the plea for burning burials, one smells everywhere 'the mould above the rose'. To those of your readers who feel after the reading, as I did, the chill of the charnel-house, let me urge an hour in the warm sunshine of the Phaedo.

But I write for another purpose—to protest against the pictures which are given of the act of dying, 'The Tortures of the Last Illness', 'The Uselessly Prolonged Torments', 'The Unbearable Memories of the Chamber of Pain', 'The Pangs of Death', 'The Awful Struggle', 'The Sharpest Peak of Human Pain', and 'Horror'. The truth is, an immense majority of all die as they are born—oblivious. A few, very few, suffer severely in the body, fewer still in the mind. Almost all Shelley's description fits:

> Mild is the slow necessity of death;
>   The tranquil spirit fails beneath its grasp,
> Without a groan, almost without a fear,
>   Resigned in peace to the necessity;
> Calm as a voyager to some distant land,
>   And full of wonder, full of hope as he.

No death need be physically painful. M. Maeterlinck has been most unfortunate to be able to say, speaking of doctors, 'who has not at a bedside twenty times wished and not once dared to throw himself at their feet and implore mercy'; but this is the same type of hysterical statement as 'all doctors consider it their first duty to protract as long as possible even the most excruciating convulsions of the most hopeless agony'. There are no circumstances contradicting the practice of Thomas Fuller's good physician: 'when he can keep life no longer in, he makes a fair and easy passage for it to go out'. Nowadays, when the voice of Fate calls, the majority of men may repeat the last words of Socrates: 'I owe a cock to Asclepius'—a debt of thankfulness, as was his, for a fair and easy passage.

HARVEY CUSHING (1869-1939)

There seems to be nothing more difficult than to know when to step down, voluntarily to retire. How painful and tragic is the spectacle of the once great man who, having hung on too long, disintegrates, unbeknown to himself, before the eyes of his horrified admirers.

Harvey Cushing, the great brain surgeon, who had some very wise thoughts on the subject of retirement wrote, at the time he was slated to be Surgeon-in-Chief of the Peter Bent Brigham Hospital in Boston, as follows to his friend Dr. Henry Christian, the new hospital's Physician-in-Chief-designate:

To Henry Christian, M.D.

November 20, 1911

Why not put the surgical age of retirement for the attending surgeon at sixty and the physician at sixty-three or sixty-five, as you think best? I have an idea that the surgeon's fingers are apt to get a little stiff and thus make him less competent before the physician's cerebral vessels do. However, as I told you, I would like to see the day when somebody would be appointed surgeon somewhere who had no hands, for the operative part is the least part of the work. Then, of course, many of us may get, vascularly speaking, a little inelastic well on this side of sixty, or may remain in this respect as youthful at seventy as are others at fifty. This is all a lottery of inheritance and habits, and I shall be very glad, for one, to have legislated to stop active work at sixty.

THOMAS W. SALMON (1876-1927)

With the appointment, in World War I, of Dr. Thomas Salmon to the post of Director of Psychiatry for the American Expeditionary Force the Army had made an excellent choice. Dr. Salmon, a psychiatrist of wide experience, and a great humanitarian with a consuming interest in the social aspects of mental disease was convinced that one of the new medical problems of the war would be the treatment and control of the war neuroses, and he accordingly focused his attention on those soldiers who had broken down mentally under the strain of their war experiences.

In some military quarters such men were regarded as being "yellow" and not deserving of medical treatment. A tragic example of the fallacy of this concept is related by Salmon's biographer. A high ranking officer, who himself had expressed such views to Salmon, appealed to him for help one day in a state of deep depression. On his way back to the United States, where he was being sent for treatment, this unfortunate man committed suicide by jumping overboard.

Writing from France to a medical officer in Washington, Salmon had the following to say about war neuroses and cowardice:

To Major Bailey

July, 1918

... Some of the actual battle cases are striking. ... A few days ago I examined sixty in one of our own Field Hospitals. One who thinks that cowardice is an essential ingredient should have seen some of them. One boy had volunteered to carry food to a detachment which had been cut off for many hours by shell-fire. The three others who went with him were killed and he developed a distinctly psychoneurotic condition. Another brought in a comrade on his back under heavy fire. He developed his symptoms when he found that his friend was dead. Another was in a dug-out when a shell entered it killing two and wounding several. He helped dig out and then brought out the wounded but became tremulous and mute a few minutes later when he saw his Lieutenant eviscerated by another shell. There are some with evident concussion symptoms and others with psychoneurotic widening or enlargement of concussion symptoms. . . .

Salmon was profoundly moved by many of his war experiences. His reaction, as a psychiatrist, to the bombing of a hospital by a German aviator is noteworthy; so are his thoughts on the effects of giving physicians "official authority" over their patients.

To his wife

July, 1918

. . . The Boche . . . reacts in his own peculiar way. I had a good chance to see it at one place where a fine little . . . hospital had been established in the gardens and lawn of a small chateau. The surgeons were operating as fast as they could in an attempt to keep up with the line of ambulances that kept coming like carriages to a fashionable wedding. The light was streaming from the big windows in the operating room, and the immense white cross of stones, 150 feet across, that marks hospitals was plainly seen on the grass. . . . The moonlight made everything distinct but a Boche flew over three times and bombed the tents. . . . What can the World do to such blind ferocity except to dispose of it for all time?

To his wife

January 17, 1919

. . . I had a conference with Mr. Fosdick about the military prison situation. He was much interested and in two weeks I am to drive with him and Mr. Baker—my first meeting with the higher-ups. The regular army medical officer keeps us "civilians" religiously away from all high line officers. I wonder what there is in organized medical work that dries up human sympathy and makes doctors deal with sick people as if they were criminals. I think ours must be a frightfully individualistic profession and that the relationship of doctor and patient ceases as soon as the doctor gains official authority over the patient. We *must* teach social medicine in the schools and we *must* make the military medical services maintain civil controls. The same tendency is just as marked in the State Hospital Service. So it must depend upon something inherent in treating patients as groups.

DAVID R. LYMAN (born 1876)

That it was possible to prevent the outbreak of serious epidemics during World War I, when millions of troops were engaged on both sides, was a remarkable feat of which medicine could indeed be proud. In former wars more men had died from infectious diseases than from war injuries. In 1914-1918 the ratios were reversed. The end effect apparently was the same....

To Charles J. Hatfield, M.D.

Dec. 31, 1919

... Our draft records have shown us more clearly than ever the havoc of chronic diseases, especially tuberculosis and venereal disease. On the other hand, the outstanding triumph of the war was the achievement of Modern Medicine working against the greatest obstacles ever known, in keeping under control those scourges which had devastated the civilian and military population alike during all previous great wars. This was possible because of years of patient research by trained investigators in the laboratories throughout the world....

HERMANN M. BIGGS (1859-1923)

The American, ever since the days of Thomas Jefferson, has been very suspicious of government interference. This general attitude, shared also by the American medical profession, explains much of the average physician's distrust of the activities of the Public Health Authorities, activities so essential for the preservation of the health of our complex modern communities.

When Dr. Hermann Biggs, an eminent proponent of preventive medical measures, stressed the advisability of periodic health examinations, a storm arose. The following letter, which Biggs felt it necessary to write in answer to his critics, is an interesting contribution to American medical thinking; it also gives an excellent picture of the status of medical practice during the first quarter of the twentieth century.

To the Press

Oct, 21, 1922

At the Annual Conference of Health Officers and Public Health Nurses of New York State held at Saratoga Springs last June I referred to the importance of periodic physical examinations, which I have long advocated as a means for the preservation of health and the prevention of diseases through early recognition and correction of defects and abnormal conditions. Comments which have since appeared in a number of newspapers indicate that serious misconception exists in some minds as to the purport of my remarks. The impression seems to have arisen that I favor an official scheme of compulsory physical examinations, to be conducted by health officers or other physicians employed by the public authorities, with the implication that every man, woman and child should be required to submit to such a periodical inquest into his or her physical conditions.

It does not seem really necessary to explain that I agree heartily with the critics of any such proposal, and that I never have and do not advocate any kind of compulsory state medical inspection of the individual citizen, except as such inspection is now carried on practically everywhere in our public schools and in charitable and penal institutions. A prying inquest by public authority into the physical condition of the adult citizen would be utterly repugnant to American ideas of individual rights, and of the proper sphere of government. The worst enemy of periodic medical examinations could choose no better means of making his opposition effective than to advocate such a fantastic plan as seems to have been read into my address at Saratoga.

So much having been made clear, I ask space to repeat my conviction that nothing is more important for the citizen who cares to keep well than that he should go of his own free will to his own physician and demand thorough examination at reasonable intervals, with the application of all the resources of modern scientific medical knowledge. This means not merely a hasty examination of the heart and lungs with the stethoscope, but a complete medical survey, including various special tests of the blood and excretions, examinations of the eyesight and hearing, as well as of the nose and throat, and often accompanied by an x-ray of the chest or other parts of the body. Adequate examination also means taking into account mental as well as physical factors, and basing conclusions on a full knowledge of living and working conditions, income, habits, recreations, and the pertinent facts of the family and personal history.

It must be obvious that such examination and advice based on it can be properly made and given only under the conditions of freedom and intimacy which are implied in the relation of the individual to his family physician. For the State to attempt thus to examine its citizens would be not only intolerable but futile, since the utmost degree of confidence and coöperation on the part of the patient is required if anything is to be accomplished. The best trained modern physicians are equipped to examine and advise their clients how to keep well, and rightly expect to be consulted for this purpose and not merely to attempt the cure of an established disease. Perhaps it is not true that the Chinese pay their doctors only to keep them well, but if this popular legend is not based on fact it was at least well invented, for it expresses the essence of the coming system and practice of civilized society. As was said recently in one of our radio health talks "The human body is the only machine for which there are no spare parts." We must learn rightly to use and carefully to safeguard those which we have. And we can best do this by picking out a competent medical adviser, consulting him frequently, believing what he says, and following his counsel. If we do this as free individuals the health of the State will largely take care of itself.

Hermann M. Biggs
State Commissioner of Health.

UNIDENTIFIED PHYSICIAN

It is difficult today to visualize the vehemence of the early opposition to psychoanalysis. To all but a few psychiatrists it was anathema, one well-known German clinician even going so far as to speak of it as a "psychical epidemic among medical men." Gradually it won adherents, became more respectable; but it is interesting that, as late as in 1924, the writer of the following very restrained letter, an academic teacher, still thought it advisable to conceal his identity.

To the Editor of *The Lancet*

Feb. 23, 1924

Some aspects of the recent development of clinical psychology seem to call for serious attention. There are medical men of repute and academic standing who practise psycho-analysis or, without practising it, regard it as containing a valuable contribution to medical knowledge. Others have adopted it as a specialty without that arduous apprenticeship which should precede specialism, and there is an uncertain number of lay analysts who make no pretence to medical knowledge. We see the daily press giving prominence to denunciations of psycho-analysis by members of our own profession, and that this takes place without protest or disclaimer indicates a sentiment which regards our psycho-analytical colleagues as without the law. Though within the narrower circle of professional discussion we no longer hear demands that psycho-analysis should be suppressed, and the tone of its opponents is more moderate than it was a few years ago, yet feeling is still so strong that some degree of courage would be required for an aspirant to professional advancement to announce his belief in the doctrine. This state of affairs has precedents in the history of medicine, and it is possible that medical history is in the making without our recognising the process.

When it is considered that the theory is now nearly thirty years old, that it has met with opposition as forcible as any in the history of scientific controversy, and that its supporters are nevertheless becoming more numerous both within and without our profession, it is plain that we are dealing with no ephemeral cult but with something possessed of strong powers of survival. It is to be noted, too, that its most conspicuous opponents are men of ripe or even advanced years, and though for a new theory to be strenuously opposed is no hall-mark of soundness, yet in other respects than this the parallel still holds good, and the comparison of Freud with Harvey and Darwin, seriously advanced by his admirers and derided by his opponents, may ultimately stand confirmed. It has been hitherto assumed that all mental processes are conscious; in fact, this assumption is given axiomatic validity and used as an a priori argument to dismiss the whole theory of the unconscious, and the discovery of its invalidity will make Freud's main theory, if ultimately incorporated with our scientific principles, a landmark in the advance of knowledge, and for the very reason that it overturns the universal assumption.

. . . One can hardly understand why psycho-analysis, if its good results are non-existent and its methods are based upon delusion, should not be allowed to die a natural death without undue fuss or attention. If, however, it stands the test of time it should greatly enrich clinical medicine and benefit a group of sufferers for whom orthodox therapy offers but little. Meanwhile we must avoid an attitude which may intimidate honest workers, especially younger men who may fear that their careers would be prejudiced if they attempted, by clinical investigation, to establish or confute the important principles involved in this controversy. And we must take care lest we afford another target for the gibe that mankind learns nothing from history.

ARNOLD C. KLEBS: (1870-1943)

Whether providing medical care for the population is a proper function of the state was becoming since the first decades of this century an increasingly controversial question in the Anglo-Saxon countries. "Socialized Medicine," as it was beginning to be called by its opponents, would spell the doom of medical science and practice, they contended. It was an absolute necessity for the preservation of the health of the community, said its proponents. And then there were some who, like Dr. Klebs, felt that it was bound to come because of social and economic developments and advised acceptance of the inevitable.

To John F. Fulton, M. D.

December 19, 1932

. . . expressing the opinion that personal medicine was bound to go, which does not mean of course that its need will be felt always and by many. I think collective efforts have to adapt themselves to natural development, in this case to the best possible regulation of impersonal medical care, and not to what we in our hearts of hearts consider a desirable ideal. Anyway this actually takes place whether we want it or not. . . .

. . . That personal medicine is a lost cause, like privacy, coziness, Gemütlichkeit, nobility . . . is proved by every step you take these days. . . . Don't you really see that our crisis is only a symptom of the vast transvaluation of all social values? We might as well accept them.

To the same

January 29, 1933

Of course you know that I am not any more than you for socialization or vulgarization (it comes to the same) of medicine. On the other hand I feel we have to do all we can to bring it about for the one and only reason that if we don't it will be done without us. If we help with it, perhaps we can manage to keep our own little corner. Machiavelli—why not? . . .

LORD BERKELEY MOYNIHAN (1865-1936)

Toward the end of 1935 there was founded in London the "Voluntary Euthanasia Legislation Society," a group whose aim it was to legalize terminating, at their own desire, the life of the incurably ill. The storm of protest which arose in many quarters was, in many instances, directed against the Society's distinguished leader, the eminent surgeon, Lord Berkeley Moynihan. In answer to a letter from an old medical friend protesting against euthanasia as being in "contravention of the canons of medical and surgical practices," Moynihan sent the following reply:

To Dr. Lobingier

(1936?)

It is just over thirty years since first we had the pleasure of meeting. Since then you and I have had occasional correspondence and I have read the many Reprints which you have been kind enough to send me. I think, however, I never had a letter which I so greatly enjoyed as that which has just come. You give me in the most tender and gracious manner a scolding for my Voluntary Euthanasia campaign.

I quite understand that there are people who take a strong objection to the lines we are advocating, but there is, in my judgement, no doubt whatever that the day is not far distant when opportunity will be given to those suffering from irremediable and excessively painful diseases of seeking relief from their agonies. The position will have to be very strongly safeguarded, of course, and we are quite willing that anything in that direction should be most strongly established. We accept the opposition from the Roman Catholic Church and we shall have to say that if this Voluntary Euthanasia is permitted the Roman Catholics are under no compulsion to apply it themselves or to any of their people.

With what you say in regard to a multitude of other diseases I most cordially agree. Step by step, or rather stride by stride we are advancing, and I have no doubt whatever that we shall, within the next decade or so, have other conquests to record, but meantime people go on suffering to an almost illimitable extent and I really think that we cannot wait for the advance which you foresee (and I agree) will come before very long.

These, however, are only comments upon one of the kindest, most generous, and most sympathetic letters I have received. I see that you do not agree with me but I hope at any rate that I have not wounded your feelings with my advocacy of what I believe to be right.

During the nineteenth century, medicine had rid itself of fruitless speculation and, in long years of arduous experimentation, had established itself on a firm scientific foundation over which its practitioners kept constant and jealous vigilance. Under such circumstances it is understandable that they had little use for "systems" which, based on unproven concepts, attempted to replace basic research by taking shortcuts. Of necessity, the "orthodox" physician had to reject the "unorthodox practitioner": the homeopath, the naturopath, the chiropractor, the faith healer, the Christian Scientist.

Moynihan, like many of his compatriots, was in the habit of writing letters to the press on topics of current and general interest, and he wrote as follows about "unorthodox medicine":

To the Press

The lay mind seems to find it unaccountably difficult to understand the professional attitude toward the unorthodox practitioner. We accept the view of Bacon that "The weakness and credulity of man is such as they will often prefer a mountebank or a witch to a physician." We do not deny to such practitioner the possession of a degree of competence in manipulative methods: we do not doubt either his sincere devotion to his task or his personal integrity, nor do we disparage the irresponsible gay confidence he has in his own very limited powers. We do not grudge him success though we recognise its extreme infrequency, and are not unfamiliar with its perilous accompaniments, its fatal disasters. Our opposition rests upon something more fundamental than this; upon his complete lack of training both in the most elementary principles which underlie all powers of diagnosis, and in the appropriate application of those principles to treatment. Such principles are not empirical, they are based upon a multitude of sciences, upon physiology, anatomy, pathology, radiology, and the like, and upon that trained clinical observation which seeks to determine not only the morbid local condition but also its correlation with the general state of the patient. It is only by such enquiry that an exact diagnosis can ever be made, and without accurate diagnosis, empirical treatment is mere guesswork, and attended by all the hazards and uncertainties of guess-work. The expert application of a method, good perhaps in itself but unsuited to the local or general condition, can bring no possible advantage and may be followed by irreparable harm. The fact that the untrained practitioner must necessarily be completely devoid of any knowledge of the nature of disease or of the methods by which it can be recognised and differentiated from those conditions whose

signs and symptoms are mimicked by it, accounts for the multitude of grievous irremediable disasters that follow far too frequently upon his treatment. These are rarely told to the world,
but doctors are very familiar with them: save for the anxiety
and expense that would be entailed it would seem to be their
clear duty to expose them.

What should we think of an astronomer who knew no
mathematics and had never seen a telescope: of a chemist who
knew nothing of the nature of the elements, or of chemical
reactions: of a physicist who spoke glibly of relativity and was
ignorant of the constitution of the atom, the second law of
thermo-dynamics or of the quantum theory? Of the unorthodox
practitioner of Medicine it is invariably true that his work and
his writing betray a complete ignorance of those fundamental
truths upon which alone a science or an art of healing can be
based.

There is surely no distinction between Medicine and those
other fusions of Science and of Art which distinguish the theory
and practice of Law, Divinity, Sculpture, or Painting. All
sciences and all arts surely require for their profitable practice
or perfect display, a stern preliminary discipline, an arduous
training under masters of experience, with the gift of inspiring
the mind or guiding the hands of the acolyte, who must "act
tomorrow what he learns to day": and whose task is

>   to watch
>   The Master work, and catch
>   Hints of the proper craft, tricks of the tool's true play.

Is it only in medical mythology that the Scientific Minerva
sallies forth fully equipped for her life's work? Is the serious
student of medicine merely wasting his time and emptying an
almost jejune purse when he devotes years of his life to most
exacting labour and to the painful acquisition of knowledge with

which more fortunate rivals claim to be endowed by birthright?

The foundations of medicine in all its branches can be acquired in one way only. We must master little by little, step by step, with unflagging grim devotion, the preliminary sciences, we must acquire knowledge of structure and function in dissecting-rooms, wards, laboratories, and come at last to the great accomplishments of diagnosis, and safe and effective and rational treatment.

Those who practise "unorthodox Medicine" are not practising "Medicine" at all. They are as competent to do so as a student would be who spoke in terms of higher mathematics without acquaintance with the elementary practice of arithmetic.

LESLIE A. FALK (born 1915)

Between the end of the eighteenth century and the beginning of the twentieth great strides had been made in combating infectious diseases. Edward Jenner's smallpox vaccination had contributed greatly toward bringing this terrible illness under control, Lister's antiseptic technique and Semmelweis' insistence on clean hands had reduced drastically the instance of "hospital gangrene" and childbed fever, Pasteur's treatment for rabies and von Behring's discovery of diphtheria and tetanus antisera had saved the lives of tens of thousands, Walter Reed's demonstration of the role played by the mosquito in the propagation of yellow fever had paved the way toward eradicating this dreaded plague, and Ehrlich and Hata's introduction of salvarsan had provided, at last, a means of successfully treating syphilis. And still there remained many serious and very prevalent infections —pneumonia, blood poisoning, typhoid fever, to name but a few—for which the existing forms of treatment were far from being satisfactory.

And then, in 1935, with the introduction of the first sulfa drug, Gerhard Domagk opened a new era in the battle against infection. Pneumonia lost, at one stroke, much of its previous peril; blood poisoning, till then very often fatal, became a much less dangerous condition and numerous other infectious diseases were made much more amenable to treatment.

During these years, more exactly since the late 1920's, there was in a London laboratory a strain of a mold which was destined to play an even greater role in the fight against infection. Doctor, now Sir, Alexander Fleming had found that the mold *Penicillium notatum* had the property of inhibiting the growth of bacteria. He published a paper on this observation and let the matter rest at that. Nine years later Professor Florey, in Oxford, in the course of other studies, took it up again.

At this point the letter of a young American medical man, Dr. Leslie A. Falk, an eyewitness of this monumental work, will continue the story.

To the Editor of *The Journal of the American Medical Association*

April, 1944

. . . In the fall of 1937 I came to Oxford as a Rhodes scholar to work in Florey's laboratory. He assigned me my doctorate thesis subject, "The Actions of Certain Bacteriolytic Principles", allowed me to choose Dr. Ernest Chain, a brilliant biochemist, as my supervisor, and bade me to get to work to isolate the substrate of lysozyme. . . . During the course of this work we began to share Florey's interest in other antibacterials of cellular origin, such as pyocyanin, actinomycin, streptothricin and bacteriophage. We read Fleming's original 1929 paper on penicillin, were most impressed with the possibilities of the subject and found it difficult to understand why the study of penicillin had practically lapsed for nine years. It appeared that this was probably due mainly to the difficulties in purification of the substance and not because the observations had not been confirmed.

We were very fortunate in being able to borrow a strain of the Fleming Penicillium notatum from another research investigator in the Sir William Dunn School of Pathology, Miss Campbell-Renton. She had kept the original Fleming strain going, hoping to work on penicillin sometime when her bacteriophage studies with Prof. A. D. Gardner did not claim all her time. With

Florey's permission, Chain and I recultured this strain and tested the antibacterial properties of the medium on several cocci. The results were not impressive. Preliminary experiments rarely are. It was a particularly busy moment in the lysozyme research, so Professor Florey asked Dr. Norman Heatley to work with Chain on the further development of penicillin. This was in 1938, as I recall. Heatley and Chain, with the active advice of Professor Florey, succeeded in purifying and standardizing penicillin, and by the late spring of 1940 hard work had produced enough partially purified penicillin for use in animal experiments. These experiments were well planned and were immediately and brilliantly successful. Classically dramatic results were obtained. The importance of the findings was understood at once, and practically the whole Sir William Dunn Institute of Pathology was turned over to penicillin research, the work being financed mainly by the British Medical Research Council. It is a tribute to the wisdom of British science and to the British people as a whole that all this was accomplished at exactly the period of the greatest peril to their country—when France capitulated and when it appeared possible that the Nazis would invade England itself. The development of the clinical use of penicillin grew rapidly, and Professor Florey's visit to the United States in the summer of 1941 stimulated interest in it here. Commercial production was undertaken, with what results is now well known. . . .

With the great technical advances made in the natural and applied sciences through the introduction of experimental methods there has been an ever-growing inordinate admiration for the practical and an almost disdainful rejection of theory and philosophy. Medicine did not escape this trend. After centuries of comparative stagnation and ineffectualness it saw discovery following discovery in rapid succession and experienced its evolution into a highly efficient science. Little wonder that it too turned to the worship of the new god, Pragmatism, with the concomitant danger of becoming a soulless craft. The following letters by a British and an American physician sound a timely warning.

JOHN GRIEVE

To the Editor of The Lancet

Oxford.
Dec. 22, 1945

. . . In the past 10-15 years medicine has achieved increasing technical perfection. The sulphonamides, penicillin, and the flavines have joined issue with the bacteria; new and improved surgical technique has made accessible seemingly remote parts of the body; electro-encephalography is a new physiological and diagnostic tool; psychosomatic medicine has attracted many fresh recruits; the natural history of disease is being studied from many angles; while statistical method has a big rôle in the evaluation of biological data. Yet, is the emphasis on technical progress not becoming too great?

We are witnessing the birth-pangs of medicine as a science— the use of the scientific method to study disease and human behaviour. Many have criticised this trend as being away from the best traditions and interests of medicine, and like most well-informed criticism this has much truth in it. If the scientific method becomes the end rather than the means, then the future is indeed gloomy.

. . . Does present-day medicine allow for contemplation and the development of a philosophy? Has the speed of the train, the car, and the aeroplane robbed the doctor of the chance afforded by his quiet ride on horseback? Would we still remember Erasmus Darwin and the Lunar Circle if these eminent men had travelled in Rolls-Royces and Meteors? The answer to this last question is without doubt "yes." These men had been brought up on, and had appreciated, the humanities in their wide sense. To them the treasures of Greece and Rome were no mere grammatical exercises but memorable for their thought content. Plato, Marcus Aurelius, and in our own tongue Shakespeare had each a message greater than the language in which it was conveyed.

The hour is late but not too late. If we are to keep philosophers in our midst, less attention must be focused on an almost exclusively scientific education at the pre-university stage. Youth and adult must be encouraged to think and see—not merely to absorb large quantities of relatively indigestible factual knowledge. G. F. Watts's picture of *Progress* is a useful illustration, though his idea was rather different: the philosopher is the man awakened and looking upward at the passage of the brilliant horseman "Progress," the technician the man searching diligently in the dust. Medicine then must have its philosophers if the patients are to be treated as human beings and not as a series of laboratory exercises.

To achieve this desirable end prospective and actual medical students should be encouraged to study the history of thought as well as the history and present-day activities of science in its broad sense. This does not mean that all must be first-class scholars of Latin and Greek. Both languages have their value in education, but it would be unfortunate if those who failed to achieve the mastery were deprived of a knowledge of the content.

Medicine with 1 percent philosophy and 99 percent technique would be almost as futile as medicine 99 percent philosophy and 1 percent technique. With the impetus of war and recent studies on atomic energy, medicine leans much more to the former than the latter. Most reactions in Nature tend towards equilibrium and this one is doubtless no exception. It is imperative, however, if medicine is to retain its soul and with it an objective that philosophy must not be relegated to the scrap-heap.

Future education in general, and medical education in particular, must be real education and stimulate thought. Granted the team of philosophy and technical excellence, medicine has a great and glorious future. Without it she must perish. To enter into our inheritance each and all of us must contribute according to his means, and no contribution can be too small.

SAUL JARCHO (born 1906)

To William Bennett Bean, M.D.

August 24, 1953

Your splendid and stimulating essay Caritas Medici has just arrived. The physicians of this country are deeply indebted to you for your efforts on behalf of important fundamentals, especially for your attempt to civilize American medicine.

After twenty years of fighting for these ideas—at times actively, more often passively—I feel that we are in a small minority and a dwindling one. And now in 1953, when the radio, which blares forth gibberish from its vacuous vacuum tubes, is yielding to television, which flashes forth darkness disguised as light, is there any positive course of remedial action which can be taken? Or must we be content to see the degree of M.D. bestowed on streamlined technical men and on carpenters of single viscera?

One major lesion lies in premedical education. It is in the undergraduate years that many young men experience that permanent narrowing of the mental field which is so characteristic of today's physician. It is in the undergraduate period that the student begins his lifelong imprisonment by the natural sciences, especially chemistry. Most men ultimately forget the chemistry and so are left in total intellectual impoverishment. They attempt to solace their declining years with golf, bridge, opera, and blindfold trips to Europe.

I propose the following remedy. The American College of Physicians and the American Board of Internal Medicine, with the aid of any other societies disposed to cooperate, should insist that the medical schools

(a) reduce the entrance requirement in chemistry

(b) accept a course in anthropology in partial fulfilment of entrance requirements

(c) demand evidence of study and attainment in the field of humane letters as partial prerequisite

(d) insist upon proof of competence in the use of written English, both as entrance requirement and as requirement for promotion and graduation.

These alterations in entrance requirements would compel the undergraduate schools to give us a better product than that which now comes off the assembly line. Doubtless the surviving

ALEX E. ROCHE

When at the end of the World War II a socialist government came to power in Great Britain one of its objectives was the introduction of tax-financed medical care. The issue had by then become also a political one and was regarded as such by many physicians.

In 1946, Alex E. Roche, a London surgeon, expressed in a letter to *The Lancet* the views of some of the political opponents among the doctors to the National Health Service Bill.

To the Editor of *The Lancet*

July 13, 1946
London

. . . Under the State system, the doctors, who, after all, will do the work, will have to accept a lower financial return, in order to pay for the necessarily gigantic bureaucratic machine.

This measure of political sadism, so alien to British tradition, is being hurried through in a moment of national mental aberration, perhaps induced by the fatigue of war.

Under the pretext of improving the national health, the thin edge of the totalitarian wedge is being aimed first at the medical profession, since doctors, being individualistic, and having no union, but only an association, are an easy prey. Once they are enslaved, the other professions and trades will surely follow them to slavery.

It would, of course, have been impolitic to start with a campaign for a State legal system, as there are too many lawyers in the House of Commons.

It is interesting to note the enthusiasm in trade-union circles for this dictatorial medical scheme, possibly due to a failure to realise that this is the first step towards a dictator State, and to forgetfulness that under full totaliarianism, as in Fascist Italy and Nazi Germany, the trade-unions were suppressed.

Incidentally the big annual financial contributions which everybody will have to make, in order to enjoy this "free" medical service, will enable those who for years have not needed medical attention to say, "Never before have so many paid so much for so little."

May sanity return before it is too late.

We have seen from earlier letters (John Collins Warren, Lord Lister) how deeply a physician's relationship to his profession can be influenced by religious tenets. The letters by Drs. Applegarth and Bacala are testimony that they still continue to do so.

J. JERROLD APPLEGARTH

To the Editor of *The New England Journal of Medicine*

Aug. 25, 1949
New York City

. . . The science of medicine is one thing. The profession of medicine is quite another. The business of a practicing physician is undeniably linked to the Christian virtue of Charity. This implies the truth of man created by God. Herein lies the inherent dignity of man. From where else comes the logic of the argument against the practice of euthanasia? The hydrocephalic or the mongol may not be apparently "useful to society," but he is "useful" to God, by virtue of being his creature. Unless doctors abandon their subtle omnipotency, and realize that the values that define their profession are Christian values, their art will be reduced to a technic. Where do doctors meet this "scientism"? At the beginning—for four full years in medical school. As a recent graduate, I can vouch for the difficulty of a medical student's viewing man as anything more than viscera, muscle groups and "integrated reflexes." The honest respect that he has for his instructor's learned outline of anatomy and physiology is easily shifted to an identification with his materialistic innuendoes and—the "organism." In all the wealth of his clinical teaching, where is he told of the practice of medicine and the values underlying it? Exhortations to "treat the patient as a whole" are not enough. He must gain an idea why the patient is worth treating at all. I urge you, therefore, to look again at the medical schools.

J. C. BACALA

To Daniel V. Dioso, M.D.

January, 1954

. . . There is also an Apologetic approach in Medicine, proving the existence of a God through the beautiful design displayed in the human body, the harmony among organs, the equilibrium among the endocrines and exocrines, between the autonomic nervous systems, etc. Whosoever designed this harmony of structure and function found in each pavement of cells, in each creature, in every generation and in the varying stages of growth and development, must be "omnipotent" to cause such all-lasting and all-perfect effects in various manners; He must be "omnipresent" as to work alike on individuals of one place and another, or of one epoch up to the present. Even in the abnormal subject of Pathology, there is the so-called *order in disorder*, for there is a criterion of diagnosis for one condition as differentiated from another, without which Pathology will be without pattern, a mass medley of confusing cases impossible each to classify. Dan, Whosoever is such Designer, He is Whom we call God.

The other day we had a discussion with the externs. They swallow whatever has been said to them by some instructors. They claim that science has been able to "create" new species. By reproduction of one specie with another formerly exposed to irradiation, a new specie was reproduced. And thus, denying

Creationism, they proceeded to prove Evolution of man from the apes. Of course, I said, "You alone" but I could not ride on their flying trapeze back to their ancestors. They mistook a monster for a new specie and purposely overlooked to account that before the matching, they needed previously created original species to work on. It was like pouring a dye in the middle of a stream, and then calling the rest of the dye-colored stream as a new specie of a river, and simply forget the original river or the original spring that flowed downstream, or the Maker of such spring streaming with uncountable H_2O's.

That is what modern researches are—time-limited and without the philosophic perspective of the untimed eternity or the untimable infinity. Oh, that I could paint with the brush of logic the picture I have of our profession in its role in the imperatives of the Eternal, above and over the selectives of the physical!

Medical science has tended to be diametrically apart from Theology, when both should be parallel and tend to meet at the Point of Infinity (Which is God). Even in most Catholic Medical Schools, they fail to staff themselves with Catholic Professors, or Catholic Authors fail to join hand and write an OB text with moral emphasis on our Faith. They seem to be apologetic about their religion. Why? The "scientians" have got them sold to the idea of looking only at what is inside the room, and not cast the eyes through the windows of thought and reason to see the vista outside. Medicine has become matter-philic and Almighty-phobic. It has become the advocate of the idea that conscience is "counter-science", or dictums of the like.

ALTON OCHSNER (born 1896)

Smoking, especially cigarette smoking, is regarded by some physicians as the cause of the unquestionable increase of cancer of the lung. Dr. Alton Ochsner, one of the proponents of the smoking theory, which is by no means generally accepted, presents his arguments in its favor in the following letter.

To a physician

May 15, 1954

. . . In 1901 cancer of the lung represented 1.1 per cent of all cancers, in 1930, 2.2 per cent, and in 1948, 8.3 per cent. . . .

The suggestion is frequently made that cancer of the lung is actually not increasing but that as a result of better diagnosis more lung cancers are being detected, whereas they were missed previously. If they were missed previously, it would mean that they were diagnosed as other conditions, such as tuberculosis. If one considers the incidence of tuberculosis in men from the ages of fifty-five to sixty-nine, which is the age at which cancer of the lung occurs, there has actually been no decrease in its incidence from 1933 to 1948, whereas cancer of the lung in this same period of time and in this same age group has increased from 18 to 120 per one hundred thousand population. . . . Cancer of the lung in females in the United States increased from 1938 to 1940 from 2.3 per one hundred thousand population to 4.7 per one hundred thousand population. This increase in the incidence of cancer of the lung in men was from 4.6 to 17.8 per one hundred thousand population.

Cancer of the lung is the only cancer in the body which does not behave as do other cancers. All other cancers in the body increase with advancing age and this is one of the reasons why cancer generally is increasing, because as a result of greater longevity more people are living in the cancer age and more develop cancer. Of all the people ninety years of age, a greater percentage will develop cancer than those eighty years of age, and of those eighty years of age a greater percentage will develop cancer than those seventy. This is true in all cancers except cancer of the lung, which increases precipitously up to the age of fifty-five and then decreases. Interestingly enough the peak age at which cancer of the lung occurs is about ten years earlier than it was fifteen years ago. I think this is due to the fact that people are smoking at an earlier age than they were fifteen years ago. The reason for the decrease in cancer of the lung after the age of fifty-five is, I believe, due to the fact that the heart and blood vessels of heavy smokers are also subjected to the noxious effects of cigarette smoking, particularly nicotine, and that as a result of the detrimental effects on the heart and blood vessels, a large proportion of individuals develop heart disease and coronary thrombosis and do not live long enough to develop cancer of the lung.

The criticism is often made that one cannot compare cancer in animals and cancer in human beings, and the inference is that any experimental work in animals is of no value. If one takes for instance the work which Drs. Graham and Wynder did on the production of cancer in animals with tobacco tar, which consisted in applying tar obtained from smoking cigarettes in almost the identical manner in which human beings smoke, to the skin surfaces of animals and after two years' application, 44 per cent of the animals developed a cancer which behaved exactly like a human cancer, the work simply shows that there is in tobacco tar a cancer-producing substance, which when applied to the skin of animals will produce cancer. It is, therefore, likely to assume that since there is a tremendous increase in the incidence of cancer of the lung and that this parallels the increase in the smoking of cigarettes and since it has shown that there is a cancer-producing agent in tobacco tar, the increase in incidence of human cancer is due to the cancer-producing factor in cigarette smoke.

ROBERT E. KAUFMAN (born 1908)

The struggle medicine had waged so successfully against the forces of destruction during World War I was continued on an even grander scale during World War II. All the new methods for the treatment of infections, in the beginning with sulfadrugs, later with penicillin, the improvements in surgery and anesthesia, the use of blood transfusions, in its infancy in 1914, and of plasma, the possibility of moving the wounded from the battlefield were all brought into play. Behind this tremendous effort were two motivations: the humanitarian one of alleviating suffering, the utilitarian one of conserving manpower. Medicine again acquitted itself magnificently.

Probably the most exacting and hazardous medical work was done by the doctors and the medical corps men assigned to the front line troops. Giving medical care under adverse conditions, frequently under fire, their problems differed from those of the men working in the hospitals behind the lines. In a letter written ten years after D-day a battalion surgeon who landed with the troops on the beaches of Normandy on June 6, 1944, gives his impressions of a sector of the medical accomplishments of the recent war.

To his son

June 6, 1954

. . . the most important "front line" measures in alleviating suffering and saving lives were, from my personal experience, the following:

1. Rapid evacuation of the wounded, less by stretcher-bearers than by jeeps and ambulances, which we had the courage to get

far forward even at considerable risk to the drivers and vehicles. One innovation we perfected in England just before D-day was the attachment of clamps on jeeps to hold stretchers so that two seriously wounded men plus several sitting patients could be transported from near the front lines to a doctor in minutes instead of hours.

2. Plasma, which we gave frequently at our aid station and occasionally even further forward. This measure to prevent shock saved many lives; in fact, only 3 men out of 1200 who reached our aid station in the first 4 months of steady combat died before reaching the medical group to our rear. Sometimes we had to prepare and inject the intravenous plasma in "black out" conditions under blankets with flashlight! I remember two of us—Dr. Tom Farris, who was later killed in action, and myself—giving this life-saving fluid into opposite arms simultaneously to get larger amounts quickly into a soldier in severe shock.

3. Morphine given early to treat pain and reduce shock. This came in metal tubes with sterile needle attached, and was so simple that we taught its use to all medical aid men and to many infantry officers. They often administered it within a few minutes after the injury, to the great relief of the wounded soldier.

4. Adequate supplies, aid stations and hospitals, and well-trained men. We never ran short of any necessary supplies, such as plasma, morphine, dressings, splints, tourniquets, etc. Also there was always enough food, fluids, clothing and vehicles. We were able to give something to eat and drink as well as blankets and sedatives to the wounded and those with "combat fatigue", so that many could return to front-line duty after a short stay at the aid station. Two of our medical department men were with each rifle company at all times to render immediate first aid and to lend moral support to the infantrymen. Replacements for doctors and enlisted men who were killed or wounded—the latter a frequent occurrence—were usually available within a few days.

ROBERT B. HOENIG (born 1913)

From the front-line aid stations battle casualties needing further care were sent to evacuation hospitals which were established behind the lines but still fairly close to the front. An impressive description of such a hospital in operation is contained in the following letter written from Brittany in August, 1944, by a young American army doctor.

To his parents

August 16, 1944

... the set up of the hospital as it functions with us in operation for wounded soldiers. Unlike maneuvers, where our tents were scattered, dispersed and camouflaged, we are now compact, in the open, and all the tents are hooked together. We are asigned to an open field and the work begins in putting up the installation.

As the patients arrive, they are processed through the receiving tent. They are given a rapid examination by a medical officer, a medical record is started, and the patient is then sent on his way. Since most of the casualties are due to wounds (rather than illness), they are sent either to a shock ward or a pre-op ward. Each of these has 40 beds and more can be crowded in without too much difficulty.

The shock patients and the more severely wounded are placed together and are given adequate therapy. Plasma, whole blood, and oxygen are used in great profusion, all to the benefit of the patient. It is remarkable to watch the patients recover when treated vigorously.

The pre-op wards are simple tents without any special equipment. In this ward, patients are readied for the operating room.

If the doctor thinks it advisable, patients are sent to x-ray for further diagnostic procedures. However, if we do not believe any such procedure is necessary, a slip is sent into the operating room desk with the patient's name and diagnosis on it, and whether or not the case is urgent.

Nearly all wounded men go first to these shock or pre-op tents. There they lie, pale and uncomplaining in the oftentimes weird and eerie shadows cast by 60 watt overhead electric lights which enable us to see what is going on in the ward. In the shock ward, most of the patients are receiving and absorbing plasma or whole blood—a miraculous strength giver. In a comparatively few minutes, the wounded soldier has recovered enough to talk with the nurse, to ask for a drink of water, or to puff a cigarette. As soon as possible, a man who has been brought out of shock is sent into the operating tent where the wounds are cleansed and debrided. We are not allowed to do primary suturing; the chances of infection are too great. Wounds are thoroughly debrided, sulfanilamide powder dusted in, vaseline gauze and dry dressing used. If it's a wound that would take less than 10 days to two weeks to recover from, to get back to duty with combat, we will keep the patient and do a secondary closure at the end of the 5th day. If we anticipate that the soldier will be unable to return to duty within 10 days, he is evacuated to England—usually by plane. When this happens, usually within 3-4 days of injury, the patient has been operated, rested in a hospital such as ours, and has returned all the way to a permanent general hospital in England.

When it comes to priority of treatment, belly cases, chest cases, gangrene (gas gangrene or other type) are given first treatment. Simple (?) perforating or penetrating wounds by shrapnel or lacerations are taken in stride after doing the more urgent cases.

In this area where we are now, (we are servicing the troops fighting for St. Malo and Dinard,) we had over 500 operative casualties in the first few hours that we were open for business. Naturally, we fall behind, and at one time we were faced with a backlog of over 250 cases that we knew we had on our hands.

In the operating room proper, we have 6 operating tables for major cases. In addition, we have set up for minor cases, which can often be done under novocaine, 4 other tables—a total of ten. It is not unusual for all ten tables to be going at the same time.

I have been surprised at the low number of the so-called horrible wounds of war. I had expected that when we went into action, we would have an untold number of ghastly wounds—faces blown off, intestines hanging out of the abdominal wall, brain tissue oozing out of the skull. On the contrary, these cases are the exception. About 90-95 percent of the wounds are of the extremities or non-penetrating type of the chest, abdomen, back or buttocks. We have done over 1400 operations, and I doubt whether we have opened the abdomen more than 50 times.

There are two explanations for this. The first is that the horrible wounds of war cause death right on the battlefield before medical aid can be given. The second, and probably better reason is that even closer to the fighting front than we are is a field hospital. They are set up to specially care for belly, chest and head cases that are too ill to be transported back to a hospital like ours. Naturally, they do a lot of major surgery on a lot of complicated cases. They save us a lot of trouble and they also save a lot of lives.

The operating room itself is hardly conducted like an operating amphitheatre in a modern metropolitan hospital. Imagine, if you can, an operating amphitheatre with 6 tables in it—all of them busy. Our tent operating room is 51 feet long and 35 feet wide. Lights, both movable and stationary, are stretched all over the place.

We scrub up for ten minutes before the first case, but after that only about two or three minutes, rinsing our hands well in alcohol after each scrub. Gloves are taken off only to scrub. Of course, we wear a cap and mask, but gowns are only worn on an obviously infected case. So, you see, we go around in our underwear tops with only gloves on for real sterility precautions.

No one scrubs with you—neither doctor, nurse nor enlisted man. There is too much work to be done to waste two medical officers and someone else on any single case unless it is real urgent or major. This method doesn't lead to real careful work, but I can say that it is definitely adequate. There are very few infections that take place though; we can tell by looking at our cases in which we do secondary closures, and those we keep around for sundry reasons. All cases are done pretty quickly, most get pentothal intravenous anesthesia or else local (few get ether), and in addition each case pre-op gets sulfa drug and penicillin. It may take up to 48 hours before we get around to operating on a patient after he is admitted to the hospital, so you can realize how important it is to give the "magic drugs". Post-op sulfadiazine is given routinely and penicillin ordered only if the doctor thinks it advisable. . . .

FREDERIC C. SHARPLESS (born 1880)

Dr. Sharpless, at the age of seventy, retired from the practice of medicine. He moved to Greensboro, Vermont, where, on a limited scale, he is—again practicing medicine! The following letter was written after his "retirement."

To the Editor of the *Journal of the American Medical Association*

March 21, 1953

. . . It is my impression that few doctors retire voluntarily, and, of those who do, few live happily ever after. The usual pattern is that the doctor, if he lives long enough, does not give up his patients; the patients give up their doctor. Too often he is deluded by his old retainers' blandishments into thinking that he is as efficient as ever and then is heartbroken when he finds they have engaged a younger man. If he is wise and has regard for his future self-esteem and happiness he will not allow such occasions to be multiplied. He will resign while he still has the confidence and friendship of his patients. At the same time he must beware of the let-down that will come when he is deprived of the daily interest and sense of importance that the medical life so abundantly provides. . . .

BIBLIOGRAPHY

William Douglass: *Collections of the New York Historical Society,* 1917, Vol. 50.

George Cheyne: *The Letters of Doctor George Cheyne to Samuel Richardson* (1733-1743), edited by Charles F. Mullet. *University of Missouri Studies,* Vol. 18.

John Mitchell: *Collections of the New York Historical Society,* 1934, Vol. 67.

Oliver Goldsmith: *Life of Oliver Goldsmith, M.B.* by James Prior, London, John Murray, 1837.

Joseph Black: *The Life and Letters of Joseph Black, M.D.* by Sir William Ramsay; London, Constable & Co., Ltd., 1918.

John Bard: *Life of Samuel Bard* by John McVickar, New York, A. Paul, Printer, 1822.

William Cullen: *An Account of the Life, Lectures, and Writings of William Cullen, M.D.* by John Thompson, Edinburgh and London, William Blackwood and Sons, 1839.

John Fothergill: *Dr. John Fothergill and His Friends* by R. Hingston Fox, London, Macmillan & Co. Ltd., 1919.

John C. Lettsom: *Memoirs of the Life and Writings of the Late John Coakley Lettsom* by T. J. Pettigrew, London, Longman, Hurst, Rees, Orme and Brown, 1817.

James Currie: *Memoir of the Life, Writings and Correspondence of James Currie, M.D., F.R.S.,* ed. by William Wallace Currie, London, Longman, Hurst, Rees, Orme and Brown, 1831.

John Warren: *The Life of John Warren, M.D.* by Edward Warren, Boston, Noyes, Holmes and Company, 1874.

Benjamin Rush: *Letters of Benjamin Rush,* ed. by L. H. Butterfield. *Memoirs of the American Philosophical Society,* Vol. 30, 1951; *Old Family Letters Relating to the Yellow Fever,* Philadelphia, J. B. Lippincot Company, 1892.

William Drennan: *The Drennan Letters*, ed. by D. A. Chart, Belfast, H. M. Sta. Off., 1931.

Edward Jenner: *Life of Edward Jenner, M.D.* by John Baron, London, Henry Colburn, Publisher, 1838.

Sir Charles Bell: *Letters of Sir Charles Bell*, London, John Murray, 1870.

John C. Warren: *Life of John Collins Warren* by Edward Warren, Boston, Ticknor and Fields, 1860.

René Laënnec: *Laënnec Avant 1806* by Alfred Rouxeau, Paris, J.-B. Baillière et Fils, 1912.

James Jackson: *Memoir of Dr. James Jackson* by James Jackson Putnam, Boston, Houghton Mifflin & Co., 1905.

James Jackson, Jr.: *Memoir of James Jackson, Jr., M.D.* by James Jackson, Boston, I. R. Butts, 1835.

Waitstill R. Ranney: *Reminiscences of the Late Waitstill R. Ranney, M.D.*, New York, 1855.

Johann Stieglitz: In *Zum Andenken and Dr. Johann Stieglitz* by K. F. H. Marx, Goettingen, Dieterich, 1846.

Samuel Hahnemann: *Life and Letters of Dr. Samuel Hahnemann* by T. L. Bradford, Philadelphia, 1895.

John Conolly: *Memoir of John Conolly, M.D.* by Sir James Clark, London, John Murray, 1869.

Sir James Y. Simpson: *Memoir of Sir James Y. Simpson* by John Duns, Edinburgh, Edmonston and Douglas, 1873.

James Hinton: *Life and Letters of James Hinton*, ed. by Ellice Hopkins, London, C. Kegan Paul & Co., 1878.

Sir William Gairdner: *Life of Sir William Tennant Gairdner* by G. A. Gibson, Glasgow, James Maclehose & Sons, 1912.

Ignaz Semmelweis: *Aetiologie, Begriff und Prophylaxis des Kindbettfiebers*, 1861.

Lord Joseph Lister: *Lord Lister* by Sir Rickman John Godlee, Oxford, The Clarendon Press, 1917.

J. Marion Sims: *The Story of My Life*, ed. by H. Marion-Sims, New York, D. Appleton and Company, 1884.

John G. Perry: *Letters from a Surgeon of the Civil War* by Martha D. Perry, Boston, Little, Brown & Co., 1906.

Mary Putnam Jacobi: *Life and Letters of Mary Putnam Jacobi* by Ruth Putnam, New York, G. P. Putnam's Sons, 1925.

Richard D. Arnold: *Letters of Richard Dennis Arnold*, ed. by Richard H. Shryock, Durham, N.C., Duke University Press, 1929.

Jean Cruveilhier: *Jean Cruveilhier* by Léon Delhoume, Paris, Librarie J.-B. Baillière et Fils, 1937.

Robert Koch: *Robert Koch* by B. Heymann, Leipzig, Akadem. Verlagsbuchhandlung, 1932.

Theodor Billroth: *Briefe*, Hannover & Leipzig, Hahnsche Buchhandlung, 1899.

Henry I. Bowditch: *Life and Correspondence of Henry Ingersoll Bowditch* by Vincent Y. Bowditch, Boston, Houghton Mifflin Co., 1902.

Thomas H. Huxley: *Life and Letters of Thomas Henry Huxley* by Leonard Huxley, London, Macmillan & Co., 1903.

Sigmund Freud: *The Origins of Psycho-analysis*, ed. by Marie Bonaparte, Anna Freud, Ernst Kris, translation by Eric Mosbacher and James Strachey, New York, Basic Books, Inc., Publishers, 1954.

Greville MacDonald: *Reminiscences of a Specialist* by G. MacDonald, London, George Allen & Unwin Ltd., 1932.

Anton Chekhov: *Letters of Anton Tchekhov to his Family and Friends*, translation by Constance Garnett, London, Chatto & Windus, 1920.

Walter Reed: *Walter Reed and Yellow Fever* by Howard A. Kelly, New York, McClure, Phillips & Co., 1906.

Sir William Osler: *The Life of Sir William Osler* by Harvey Cushing, Oxford, The Clarendon Press, 1925.

Harvey Cushing: *Harvey Cushing* by John F. Fulton, Springfield, Illinois, C. C. Thomas, Publisher, 1946.

Thomas W. Salmon: *Thomas W. Salmon, Psychiatrist* by Earl D. Bond, New York, W. W. Norton & Co., Inc., 1950.

Herrmann M. Biggs: *The Life of Herrmann M. Biggs* by C.-E. A. Winslow, Philadelphia, Lea & Febiger, 1922.

Lord Berkeley Moynihan: *Berkeley Moynihan, Surgeon* by Donald Bateman, New York, The Macmillan Co., 1940.

INDEX

Addison, Thomas, 98
Advice to young physicians, 25-27, 66, 67, 93, 99, 120
American Medical Association, Journal of the, 236, 257
Andral, Gabriel, 100
Anesthesia
  ether, introduction of, 92, 123
  chloroform, introduction of, 127
  dangers of, 160
  early opposition to, 128
Antisepsis, 151
Antitoxin
  diphtheria, 198, 204
  tetanus, 198
Applegarth, J. J., 245
Arnold, R. D., 170, 171
Asclepius, 216
Auscultation, 95-97, 104

Bacala, J. C., 246
Bacon, Roger, 3
Bailey, Pearce, 218
Bacteriology, early work in, 174-176
Bard, John, 25-27
Bard, Samuel, 25-27
Bean, W. B., 240
Beck, Carl, 207
Beddoes, T. L., 109
Behring, Emil, 198
Bell, Sir Charles, 86, 87
Bell, George, 49
Biggs, H. M., 222
Billroth, Theodor, 177, 178
Black, Joseph, 20
Black Death, 4
Blood-poisoning
  in childbed fever, 147
  after surgical operations, 150

"Body-snatching," 90
Boerhaave, Hermann, 4, 173
Boswell, James, 45
Boston, (Mass.), 7-9, 8-9, 90, 91, 123, 127, 180
Bowditch, H. I., 180-183
Boylston, Zabdiel, 8
Breslau (University), 174, 175
British and Foreign Medical Review, 123
British Medical Research Council, 237
Brown-Séquard, C. E., 188
Brussels, 86, 88
Buffalo
  Medical College, 135
  Medical Journal, 135
Bonaparte, Napoleon, 4
Burnie, W. G., 191
Burns, Robert, 49

Cambridge (Mass.), 25
Cancer
  "cures," 30
  of the lung, 248 ff.
  theories of
    pollution of rivers, 190
    increased consumption of meat, 191
    cigarette smoking, 248
Carbolic acid, 151
Chain, Ernest, 236
Charcot, J. M., 195
Charleston (S.C.), 170
Chekhov, Anton, 200-202
Cheyne, George, 11-15
Childbed fever (puerperal fever), 3, 70, 146 ff.
Chloroform, 127, 128, 160
Cholera, 3, 105, 106, 176